CW00418425

£3.99
WK52

TALES FROM THE 'DAWN HUNTER'

Featuring the fishy stories of Skipper Wullie
'Clane and crew

*INCLUDES FISHING LORE AND RARE PHOTOGRAPHS FROM
THE GOLDEN ERA OF HERRING RING NETTING AND PAIR
TRAWLING ON THE SCOTTISH WEST COAST*

FREDDY GILLIES
Illustrations by Davy Cowan

By the same author

In Campbeltown Once More
Boyhood memories of 'The Wee Toon' during the 1950's and 60's

Life on God's Island
Stories from the Inner Hebridean Island of Gigha

Life with the Coal Tar
Stories from Campbeltown's West Coast fisherfolk.

Available from book and craft shops or s.a.e. to Famedram
Publishers, Mill Business Centre, PO Box 3, Ellon, AB41 9EA

ISBN: 0905 - 489667

NORTHERN BOOKS FROM FAMEDRAM, ELLON
AB41 9EA www.northernbooks.co.uk

Printed by Printall, Firhill, Glasgow.

Front cover

The former Campbeltown fishing vessel *Alliance (CN 187)* is surrounded by hungry seagulls after hauling her herring pair trawl near Arran in partnership with another local boat *Aquila (OB 99)*. Oban photographer David Livingstone took the picture from the research vessel *Calanus.*

Back cover

Photographed by Ian McDonald in 1994 is the *Summer Morn (B58)*. Skippered by the author, the vessel was participating in the North Sea scallop fishery and is seen going through her paces on the approaches to Stonehaven Harbour following a paint-up at the East Coast port.

ACKNOWLEDGEMENTS

I would like to thank sincerely the following people for their valued help in the preparation of this unusual little fishing book.

Most of the herring ring-net photographs came from the albums of Lachie Paterson, Carradale, and Lochgilphead's John Crawford, to whom I am grateful for being allowed to rummage through their treasured collections, which, as well as examples of their own work, contain pictures from the following sources: British Maritime Museum; Glasgow Museum of Transport (Dan McDonald collection); Angus Martin, Sinclair Blair, Mrs Betty Cockburn, Cecil Finn and Donald Gillies, all Campbeltown; James L.Campbell, John McConnachie and Walter McConnachie,Carradale; Clive Munro and Hugh McPhee, Ayrshire; Bill Tudhope, Invernesshire; Other photographs were contributed by John McFadyen, Campbeltown; Neil MacAlister, Gigha; David Livingstone, Oban; Ronnie Brownie, Carradale; Jonti Ancell, Tarbert and Andrew Denholm, Invernesshire. Mr Billy Gilchrist, of Campbeltown, provided local place names and his daughter, Mrs Jennifer Kelly, kindly supplied the words of the *Campbeltown Fisherman's Alphabet* and the song *In Campbeltown Once More*. For his explanatory piece on a wonderful poem entitled *The Flight*, I especially thank Campbeltown's well-known author/poet, Angus Martin.

CONTENTS

Part one

Part two

FOREWORD

Though the characters and stories in this book are entirely fictional, the *Dawn Hunter* is crewed by men from Campbeltown, where the boat is based.
In order to introduce a measure of authenticity, the reported speech throughout is written in the local dialogue.
Guttural Lowland Scots blends with a lingering trace of Highland lilt and a touch of Northern Irish brogue to produce an unusual accent that is somewhat unique. I hope the following short explanatory notes will be of benefit to the reader.
Pronunciations of the vowels more often than not take a wayward slant from the accepted norm. Invariably *i* before *tion* is changed to *ee* so that competition becomes *competeetion*, position becomes *poseetion* and so on. The letter *i* is also turned into *u* in other instances. Jim is known as *Jum* and a chimney is a *chumney*. Also, *ike* and *yke* alter to *aik* to change words such as like to *laik* and dyke to *daik*.
"He can swum laik a fush," is a typical phrase.
A before *ke* is changed to *eck* to produce words like *heck* (hake); *reck* (rake); *Jeck* (Jake); ceck (cake).
The *ow* combination becomes *oo* and examples are *oolet* (owlet); *boolin'* (bowling); *croon* (crown); *tooell* (towel).
A is added to the hard *o* to give *hoarn* (horn); *boarn* (born); *moarnin'* (morning). Some words ending with the letters *ay*, for example day and play, are pronounced *deh* and *pleh*.
U in some cases is replaced by *ee* making burial sound like *beerial* and busy changes to *beesy*.
Ea is said as a hard *e* to make pear become *perr*, bear to *berr* and tear to *terr*.
There are also certain words, which to the best of my knowledge are restricted to the Campbeltown dialect. *Ee noo* means just now, picked becomes *puck* and a canine is known as a *doag* - not to be confused with its central Scottish cousin *dug*.
A *queef* is an unpleasant person and *gyadds* suggests that someone has just seen or smelt something offensive. If a person is described as being a *gaalawf*, usually preceded by a hearty expletive, the description is anything but complimentary. Similarly, if one is unfortunate enough to be called a *dallooed*, then the implication is, indeed, nasty.

The word *wild* is used peculiarly as an adjective to give emphasis to a statement. "*It's a wild quiet night,*" is an example. A person, too, can be *wild and quiet*. *"The dance was wild and good,"* does not necessarily mean that the function played host to any form of ribaldry, but passed off as an enjoyable event. The Royal Burgh of Campbeltown, is known to many local residents as *Snecka Buie,* though I do not know why.

A post war addition to the local dialogue and now in widespread use is the expression *cat melodeon.* Shortened simply to *cat,* it is a derogatory description of either a person or an event, for example: "*That gemme o' futba' wis cat.*" Perhaps the most classic example of Campbeltown singularity is the word *hoot,* which is used in preference to *what.* I am reasonably certain that one will never hear the question: "*Hoot the Hell dae ye think yer plehin' at?*" anywhere in the universe other than the Campbeltown area.

The prefixes *Mac* or *Mc* are dropped from surnames so that men with names such as Peter MacDonald, William MacDougall and Neil MacIntyre are known as *Peter Donal', Wullie 'Dougall* and *Neilly 'Tyre,* who also loses the first two letters of *Intyre.* Ian MacLeod, for some reason, becomes *Ian Gloud* and John MacLean is referred to as *Jocky 'Clane.*

Almost everyone in the area has been given some form of nickname, perhaps stemming from schooldays or as a result of a particular incident in later life. Some are funny, while others are cruelly defamatory.

The second part of the book is a uniquely comprehensive photographic record of Clyde herring ring net and pair trawl vessels - pictured both at home and in Hebridean waters - local prawn trawlers and scallop dredgers. Also included are items of local fishing folklore and the section is devoted to all Clyde fishermen, past and present.

GLOSSARY

Autopilot: electrical device connected to hydraulic steering gear that enables boat to maintain course unaided.

Black fish: illegally landed fish taken when Government-imposed quotas are exhausted.

Boring (tide): steaming against the effects of the tide.

Buggerment: local word for high-spirited nonsense and not, as perhaps suggested, of a more serious implication.

Bulkheads: interior wall-like divisions of a boat.

Cailleach (Gaelic): old woman

Clam or King Scallop: bi-valve shellfish that contains succulent meat and roe.

Cod-end: Tailpiece of a trawl net that is secured by a special slipknot.

Dooker: cormorant. Tarbert fishermen are also known collectively as *Dookers*.

Fathom: six feet.

Gleogair (Gaelic): stupid fellow.

Green: any member of the codfish family.

Heidbanger: Idiot.

Laldy: vigorously expressive.

Puckle (or wheen): unspecified smallish amount.

Purse-seiner: 100-foot plus herring or mackerel boat.

Crechan: Queen scallop, which is smaller than the King scallop but nonetheless equally tasty and much sought after culinary delight.

Ring net: a once popular method of herring fishing by two purpose built boats. Now completely defunct, ring netting was superseded by pair trawling in the early 1970's.

Rockhopper net: trawl which, as the name implies, is used for fishing on firm and stony ground.

Saar: moderate breeze of wind.

Saarach (a): trouble with boat or gear.

Scran: illicit gains.

Ship's husband: shore-based person responsible for ordering provisions, fuel, ice etc.

Shullin' (shilling): equivalent to 5p in the former UK currency.

Shooting (nets): casting the gear into the sea.

Terr (tear): ploy or amusing practical joke.

Tiravee: a form of fit.

Topstrake: topmost plank on wooden hulled boat.

Tow: term used to describe the duration of a haul during trawling operations.

Trum (trim): mood or fettle.

Unit (of herring): modern 100kg measure of herring, which, on adoption of the metric system, replaced the basket and cran.

Warps: flexible steel wires that connect the net to the boat when trawling.

Wulk: periwinkle.

THE VESSEL

The MFV *Dawn Hunter* (CN 171) is a solidly built wooden multi-purpose trawler of typical Scottish design and layout. Below decks, an engine room situated forward of a spacious aft cabin houses a Caterpillar engine of 365 horse power which gives her a respectable speed of ten knots.

Fifty-six feet long, the *Dawn Hunter* is fitted out with a chilled fish room to carry both boxed fish and bulk catches such as sprats or herring.

The boat's wheelhouse contains an array of electronic fishing and navigational aids. She is equipped with radio, radar, sonar, colour echo sounder, video track plotter, automatic pilot and satellite navigation system.

Deck machinery includes a hydraulic winch with a ten-tonne pull, which holds the trawl warps, and a crane for heaving the nets aboard.

Painted in her skipper's favourite colours of burgundy with a mid-oak topstrake, the *Dawn Hunter* fishes, on a seasonal basis, for prawns, white fish, scallops and herring.

THE CREW

The *Dawn Hunter's* skipper-owner was baptised William Andrew Maclean, but is known along the western Scottish seaboard as *Wullie 'Clane*. He is a married man of 47, the father of two children.

Wullie is a hard-worker determined to succeed, but he also possesses a strong sense of humour. He is particularly adept at getting his crew to put in that little bit of extra effort through pure West Highland flattery, largely unnoticed by the deckies.

Also an opportunist, not many moneymaking schemes, however unlikely, escape his notice.

The vessel's mate is 38-year-old Sandy Carmichael, a father of three. Easily the meanest of the *Dawn Hunter's* crew, he wouldn't, according to Wullie, "Pee doon yer throat if yer lungs wur on fire."

If it were at all possible to be serious-minded aboard the *Dawn Hunter*, Sandy, though by no means a morose character, would be the nearest contender. His leisure time passion is skin-diving and he spends many hours exploring sunken wrecks for items of value.

Cameron MacPherson, the engineer, allows only two other interests to divert his attention from his beloved Caterpillar marine propulsion unit - practical jokes and girls. Strikingly handsome and in his prime at 27, Cameron treats life as one huge joke, sometimes to the extreme consternation of his shipmates. Among the eligible young bachelors of Campbeltown, he is probably the most successful with the girls.

Waging constant war against the voracious appetites of his shipmates is 19-year-old Angus Robertson. Though he comes from a family with no fishing connections, Angus loves the life at sea and was fortunate in obtaining a berth with Wullie on leaving school; he is often the target of Cameron's jokes.

This collection of little light-hearted stories is concerned more with the diversionary antics of the *Dawn Hunter*'s crew rather than actual fishing operations, but they do find the time occasionally to put their trawling skills to good use!

CAMERON AT LARGE

Wullie heaved an exasperated sigh of resignation. It was only Monday morning and, as he guided the *Dawn Hunter* towards the prawn fishing grounds in the Firth of Clyde, he knew from past experience that anything could happen in the week that lay ahead.

The circumstances leading to his premonitions of wholesale tomfoolery had begun a couple of hours earlier, when he arrived at Campbeltown's Old Quay to prepare for the week's toil and discovered a neatly bound package dangling from the wheelhouse door handle. A small card bore the legend: '*To Skipper Maclean from the grateful crew of the Scooby Doo.*'

Even the most uneducated eye could discern that the package contained a bottle, probably filled with a nice drop of spirits; a wave of anticipation swept over Wullie as he tore at the wrapping.

The owner of the Scooby Doo had indeed, cause to be grateful to Wullie and his crew, for, two days previously they had encountered the pleasure craft stuck on a sandbank at the entrance to Campbeltown Loch. A gentle tug on a nylon rope leading from the *Dawn Hunter* to the stranded vessel was all that was required to refloat her but the yachtsmen were loud in their praises of skipper Maclean and the "superb display of seamanship" shown by him in effecting the rescue. Wullie basked in the somewhat undeserved glory and accepted a generous dram aboard the *Scooby Doo* later.

"We'll get you something for your trouble, skipper," he was told by one of the party.

"Och, ye needna bother. It wis naethin' really," replied the skipper who at the same time told himself inwardly with typical West Highland guile that if the yachters had not been so affable and hospitable, the *Scooby Doo's* insurers would have been contacted.

"Now there you are," muttered Wullie to himself as he peeled off the paper wrapping to reveal a gleaming bottle of 10-year-old Bowmore Malt.

The remainder of the crew arrived aboard in varying states of recovery from the weekend's excesses and the *Dawn Hunter* cast off for the sheltered passage down Campbeltown Loch to Davaar Lighthouse, where she met the open sea. Angus busied himself with the Monday morning chore of stowing away the week's provisions and was thus occupied for a while before boiling up the kettle for a brew of strong tea. Wullie eventually received a steaming mug from the cook and reckoned that a small sensation of the malt added to the beverage would not go wrong.

Though by no means a drinker at work, Wullie decided to take a small sample by the neck first and almost choked when the foul-tasting concoction assaulted his taste buds. It appeared that the main constituent of the bottle was ancient cold tea but something even more unpleasant had been added to give it a bit of extra bite.

Suspicion, rightly, fell upon Cameron, who was sitting in the galley drinking tea and quite oblivious to his skipper's coughing fit. Not for one moment did he think that Wullie had already sampled the devilish brew.

When he had recovered sufficiently from his exertions, Wullie left the *Dawn Hunter* on autopilot for a few minutes and came through the dividing door between the wheelhouse and mess deck.

Clutching the bottle, he made for Cameron and said: "Here ye go, a wee taste o' real whusky tae take the chill oot o' the moarnin'. Ye'll laikley be needin' a reviver efter the weekend anyweh."

The speed with which the engineer's hand covered his mug would have made a stage magician proud as he simultaneously announced: "Easy, Wullie. Ah'm off the drink since Setterdeh an' ah'm only takin' gin fae noo on."

Angus and Sandy, both in on the ploy, also politely declined the skipper's invitation to join him in a wee drop of the *cratur.*

"Boys a dear, youse is gettin' aawful releegious right enough," observed Wullie as he returned to his position at the helm.

The other three made magnanimous efforts to contain themselves and Cameron said he would give Wullie the genuine bottle, which the yacht owner had asked him to pass on, at the weekend.

Meanwhile, the offensive liquid was plummeting its way to a 25 fathoms grave through an open wheelhouse window as Wullie pondered on what possible *buggerment* Cameron might get up to in the days that lay ahead.

The preparation of Tuesday's breakfast provided the answer. Canned mushrooms and baked beans featured often on the morning menu and Angus fished out two large tins of each from his dry stores locker. To his utter consternation, the first one he opened contained a succulent brand of pears and not, as stated on the label, beans. The next tin produced an equally luscious quantity of strawberries. Turning to the mushrooms, the opened cans revealed two generous portions of custard instead of the tasty breakfast accompaniment.

Looking on with interest, Cameron commented: "Well, ah've seen many a thing in mah deh, but this takes the buscutt. Or should it be the strawberry?"

"Hoot the dickens dae ye think heppened?" inquired a most concerned cook. "Ah`ll bet ye any money the computers at the factory took a tiravee. It's aal computers nooadehs. This jeest shows ye nivver tae trust a computer," was the engineer's explanation.

"Ah`ll show them bloody computers," said an outraged Angus. "Ah`m gaan tae write tae that team an' tell them hoot ah think o' their computers."

"You dae that Angus, son. Gie them laldy an' tell them they spoiled the brekkfast on a good Chrustian boat," advised Cameron.

As the week wore on and Angus required dinner desserts, beans and mushrooms appeared out of fruit and custard tins, further enraging an already irate cook.

With his anger directed solely at the food-processing firm, Angus was incapable of working out a rational explanation. He completely overlooked the fact that there could be another source to the problem - such as the engineer's dexterity in the art of transferring the paper labels from one tin to another.

Angus later contacted the company and eventually received a letter of apology from a totally bemused quality control manager along with a complimentary case of assorted tinned goods, all properly labelled.

Wednesday of that week saw the *Dawn Hunter* move closer to the Ayrshire coast, where a decent fishing of prawns was taking place. That evening's landing was made at the port of Troon, which pleased the crew, as they liked a run ashore there.

A familiar figure appeared on the quayside as the catch was being swung ashore. Andy Toner, an endearing middle-aged rascal had befriended the *Dawn Hunter*'s crew some years previously and had appointed himself *ship's runner*. He attended to the supply of fresh milk and bread when the boat was in port in return for a few stones of fish that he filleted for sale in various pubs, the proceeds of which were converted into beer with some gusto.

Andy had one distinct disadvantage in the eyes - or noses - of the crew, in the form of a peculiar odour that hung about his person, the result of an unhealthy disregard for personal hygiene.

It was, therefore, with some reluctance that they agreed to suffer the olfactory horror and granted a request from him to be allowed to spend a day at sea aboard the *Dawn Hunter*, having failed to dampen his enthusiasm by various means.

"There's a gale on the wireless," warned Wullie quite falsely.

"Ah wis roon Cape Hoarn oan a merchantman thirty years ago." came the quick fire retort.

"Ah`m only gled ah wisna sharin' a cabin wae him," muttered Sandy barely out of earshot. Sandy was easily the most fastidious of the *Dawn Hunter's* men when it came to cleanliness, both personal and otherwise.

Angus tried with: "Och, it's a wild miserable job the prawns. Ye'r up tae yer eyes in mud screwin' the heids off them aal deh long."

This only served to fire Andy with even more keenness for the excursion and he informed Wullie that he would be down at three am with morning rolls "straight oot the baker's ivven."

True to his word, Andy turned up on the quayside at the appointed hour cradling two dozen still warm rolls and the *Dawn Hunter* set off on yet another prawn search.

All hands turned their attention to the rolls and mugs of tea before Wullie asked Sandy to steer the boat while he retired below for a nap as the boat steamed to the predetermined shooting point some two hours distant.

Wullie was joined in the cabin presently by Cameron, Angus and their day visitor. "Ye might as well turn in for an 'oor Andy," said Cameron with a twinkle in his eye as he shot a noticeable sidelong glance in the direction of Sandy's bunk.

The *Dawn Hunter* was fitted out with six bunks, but two were crammed to capacity with all manner of things to such an extent that a mouse would have difficulty in finding a space to curl up in.

Sandy was meticulous in the way he kept his bunk. It was done out with sheets, soft pillows and duvet, all taken ashore each weekend for washing.

Three berths were now occupied and Andy, attired in greasy anorak, stained jeans, muddy training shoes and with a head sorely in need of a shampoo, rolled into the mate's empty bed.

When Sandy ran out of cigarettes an hour later he had occasion to visit the cabin in order to replenish his stock and was almost plunged into apoplexy when he saw the snoring, open-mouthed Andy horizontal on his bed.

"Get tae hell oot o' that bunk at wance, ye fulthy owld bugger," expostulated the outraged mate, whose voice could be clearly heard above the growl of the big Caterpillar engine.

The other three residents of the cabin, awakened from light slumber, chuckled quietly to themselves in their curtained-off bunks.

Catnapping between hauls was standard procedure aboard the boat and Andy spent such time later that day stretched out on the cabin seat locker. His ability to revert from full consciousness to a coma-like state within minutes astonished the crew and Cameron decided to see how far he could go without rousing the sleeping Andy. Liberally coating his fingers with soot from the cabin *Jack Tar* stove, Cameron outlined a magnificent set of moustache and goatee beard on Andy's countenance. The comatose guest dozed on - and all the time dreaming of his favoured waterfront tavern.

Once again on deck, the crew only had to look in Andy's direction to set off yet another series of sidesplitting guffaws.

"Aw, come oan. Tell me the joke an' we'll aw laugh," pleaded a mystified Andy.

Fish buyers and porters at the Troon market that night had to look twice at Andy, a character well-known to them, as he assisted the *Dawn Hunter*'s crew in the unloading of the catch.

"Dae ye think ye'll haive a wee waash an' shave afore ye go for yer pints the night?" Wullie enquired as Andy prepared to go ashore with his ration of fish fillets.

"Och, ah canny be boathered. Ah'll dae it later on at hame," was the expected reply.

The talk of shaving triggered off yet another ploy by the engineer.

The *Dawn Hunter* complement made a habit of going ashore for a short spell when in Troon on Thursday nights, with all hands in high spirits in anticipation of the short Friday working day and the coming weekend. Each man shaved and donned clean jumpers and jeans before partaking of modest refreshment in their favourite pub, the clientele of which was made up almost entirely of members of the seafaring fraternity.

Making sure that his shipmates were busily engaged in other matters, Cameron slunk into the galley and removed four day's growth from his face at rapid speed. Thus accomplished, he proceeded to lather the salient parts once more before hiding the bag of disposable razors that were used on a communal basis.

One by one his crewmates came in off the deck and Cameron made an exaggerated show of hunting for the razors, which had mysteriously *gone missing*.

"Och, that eediot in the shop must have forgot tae putt them in wae the stores," lamented the engineer.

"They were definitely there on Mondeh moarnin' for ah mind fine o' puttin' them aweh," Angus stated firmly.

"Well, they're naw there noo. An' ah'll tell ye somethin' else, it's naw gaan tae stop me shavin'," said Cameron.

The engineer slid open the galley cutlery drawer and withdrew a vicious-looking ten-inch long bread knife. Standing in front of the mirror mounted on the bulkhead he went through the motions of shaving - skilfully removing the soap and nothing else.

Angus gazed at Cameron with wide-eyed incredulity and asked: " Is it naw sore on yer face?"

"Not at all, ah'm gettin' wan o' the closest shaves ah've ivver had," stated Cameron.

The results of his labours had, of course, all the hallmarks of a perfect shave and he whistled gaily as he rinsed off and patted his face dry.

Two minutes later, the cook, filled with a youthful concern that the young Ayrshire lassies might be put off by his unsightly stubble, had to be stopped from inflicting serious injury upon himself as he prepared to shave with the huge blade.

"Och, see you, yer a bloody heidbanger," he told Cameron when the engineer handed him a safety razor taken from the *missing* bag.

As he made his way home on Friday evening, Wullie was in fine fettle. He reflected on a good week's fishing with a few laughs thrown in and decided that life on the *Dawn Hunter* would be much duller without Cameron, despite his penchant for playing practical jokes. He chuckled to himself on recollecting an onboard incident the previous day when the engineer had further bamboozled young Angus by secretly inserting an egg in a frozen chicken's rear cavity. Walking along, Wullie allowed his canvas holdall to swing lightly from his fingers in time with his sailor's gait. He was blissfully unaware that an alarmingly explicit girlie magazine, which his wife would discover when she sorted through his soiled fishing clothes for laundering later that night, had mysteriously found its way into his kit.

ONE POTATO, TWO POTATO, THREE POTATO.....

Eating aboard the *Dawn Hunter* was a function taken very seriously by the four shipmates. Huge fried breakfasts were followed by frequent and substantial snacks before a massive dinner was prepared.

Angus had by this time attained a degree of competence in the galley which was much appreciated by the other three, although, as a raw young cook just out of school, he was the perpetrator of a few culinary disasters.

Cameron had told Angus when he joined the boat that all hands liked a "wild big brekkfast" to set them up for the day and he was to be sure to "make bulk." The cook's first creation of charred bacon and eggs, served with crisply fried herring and topped with a generous helping of tinned macaroni cheese was left untouched - a matter which both perplexed and mystified Angus. After consuming an emergency breakfast of three plates of cereal, Cameron suggested with his finest irony: "It might have gone doon a wee bit better if ye had served it up wae mashed potatoes an' turnip son."

"There's naw a bit o' turnip on the boat but ah can soon boil a dose o' tatties for youse," offered the anxious-to-please cook. A swipe across the ear from Cameron's baseball cap quickly dispelled that notion.

The following morning Cameron decided to familiarise the youthful Angus with the basics of boat cooking and introduced a little light relief into the proceedings when it reached the egg frying stage. The *Dawn Hunter* was rolling gently through no more than five degrees but the engineer fully convinced the cook that something would have to be done to completely stabilise the boat so that the eggs would set in the frying pan.

"Aweh up intae the wheeluss an' tell Wullie ah'm fryin' the eggs an' he'll need tae keep the boat stiddy an' stop her rockin' aboot," said Cameron barely able to stifle a snigger.

Wullie listened to the earnest request from the *Dawn Hunter*'s latest recruit with a sympathetic ear and said: "Och, ah'll dae ma very best but King Canute tried somethin' similar a puckle o' centuries ago an' he didna haive very much luck."

On his return to the mess deck, Angus saw the perfectly formed eggs - effortlessly cooked by Cameron — and he believed absolutely that the skipper held some mystical power over his boat. He wondered deeply how Wullie could control her sea behaviour at a touch, and it was quite some time before Cameron enlightened him.

On one occasion Wullie exchanged a stone of haddock with a scallop boat for two dozen large clams. Clams are particularly tasty when fried quickly in bacon fat and eaten with other breakfast items and Wullie gave Angus somewhat vague instructions to "make them alang wae the brekkfast."

At the appointed hour a huge ashet containing the unshelled scallops was placed ceremoniously on the mess deck table beside the sausage, bacon, eggs and black pudding. In his ignorance, Angus had boiled the clams furiously for an hour in a huge pot, quite oblivious to the fact that the edible meat had to be extracted from the cast iron shell before cooking. Thinking he might be able to salvage a few morsels, Sandy prized open a clam to find that the entire inner contents of meat and offal had disintegrated together into a fine pulp.

Angus's first attempt at cooking steak mince culminated in his despatch to a Chinese take-away shop in Girvan in order that his shipmates might be saved the onslaught of malnutrition. 'Sma' beefies,' as mince is known on all Scots fishing boats, is always a popular dish afloat and Angus had a vague notion that it was important to add water to the simmering saucepan. The copious quantity he used, however, had anything but the desired effect and a very hungry and irritated Cameron poured the resultant pot of mince soup into Girvan harbour.

Wullie imposed a ban on a lesser-known brand of tinned steak and kidney pie following Angus's discovery that it was an extremely convenient meal to prepare. A can opener, after all, was hardly a difficult instrument to operate and a short time in a hot oven saw the pies ready for the table.

Intended for use only as an end of trip snack or when on prolonged bad weather anchor mooring, Angus produced such a dinner one evening.

Sandy, whose appetite was matched only by his almost fanatical tight-fistedness, enjoyed his usual prodigious feast but made a fatal misjudgement by commenting: "That wisna' too bad fur a wee change."

The regularity with which the pies appeared thereafter, accompanied by reconstituted potatoes and tinned vegetables, resulted in near mutiny on the mess deck.

Cameron reckoned the pies' ingredients could be likened to the inside of a certain primate's cranium and he told Angus in no uncertain terms: "If ah see wan merr o' them bloody gorilla's heids on the boat ah'll scream. They're startin' tae mind me o' the time ah went hame drunk wan night an' nearly ett a tin o' doag meat thinkin' it was stew."

Wullie was also thoroughly disgusted with the tinned pie and he later calmed the situation by advising the shopkeeper who supplied the boat's provisions to somehow *forget* to include them when making up the order.

Probably the cook's worst offence against the three seafaring epicureans was committed on the day he stewed several undersized, unfilleted saithe, or *gleshans* as they are known, in a pan brimming with canned tomato soup.

However, by trial and error and having listened to his mother's advice, Angus was now quite capable of producing tasty and nourishing meals that were, on occasion, even quite delectable. Hygiene in the galley, too, had improved tremendously and he no longer spat into the chip fat to test the temperature or stirred the peas with his fingers.

The four men were enjoying a pleasant repast one October night whilst lying alongside Islay's Port Ellen pier, having finished a successful day's work at the prawn fishing near Chuirn Island, and the usual big pot of potatoes occupied a considerable space on the table.

"Aye boys, it's a grett thing a tattie. It's a peety ah canna manage tae eat them the wey ah used tae," said Wullie spearing his eighth. "Mind you, Sandy here is aboot the best ah've seen at them, is that naw right Sandy?"

The mate, steadily munching his way through a plateful of casseroled steak, potatoes and two veg, answered between mouthfuls: "Ah believe ah could manage twunty at a push."

"Ah heard o'a fella on Jura that wance ett therty-three," Cameron mentioned innocently.

"Nae man can eat therty-three tatties at a sittin'," stated Sandy.

"Well, it was his ain cousin that telt me aboot it when ah left her hame fae a dance in Carradale wan night."

"Supposin' it was the Almighty himsel' that said it ah still widna believe it." Throwing down the gauntlet, the undisputed champion potato eater of the Campbeltown fleet, brimming with supreme self confidence, continued: "If ah ivver come across this fella ah'll challenge him tae a contest, ferr an' squerr. If ah wisna eatin' anythin' else alang wae the spuds ah think ah could manage therty."

Wullie, listening with interest, notified his mate that he could well have the chance to consolidate his position the following week.

"By the look o' the tides ah think we'll be fushin' the hard grunn off the Jura shore. We'll laikley be in Cregusses (Craighouse) at night so ye'll maybe see yer man then," he said.

That weekend, Wullie rang his Jura friend, lobsterman Lachie Morrison to inquire about the prowess of the island's potato eating king.

"Now, I would not like to put a number to it Wullie, but he'll certainly eat a damned good few," Lachie informed him.

Before the telephone conversation ended, Wullie and Lachie had decided to stage a duel between Sandy and his adversary, one Davy Munro, a man quite unknown to the *Dawn Hunter*'s crew.

"Now you chust leave everything to me Wullie. Mind an' be sure to be in on Wednesday, that's all. And do you fancy a wee £25 bet on the result?"

The wager was agreed upon and the two friends, each quietly confident of lifting the winnings, wished each other luck for the following week's fishing.

The contest turned out to be something of an event. Lachie, always on the lookout for ways to inject a spark of life into the island's quiet winter existence, secured the use of the Craighouse village hall as the venue and organised a ceilidh to follow, which he advertised on crude posters in the local hotel and shop.

A chain reaction of betting on the outcome of the tussle was sparked off on the Monday when Cameron and Angus, both delighted with Wullie's news of the forthcoming battle, asked him to relay their stake to Lachie on VHF radio. Lachie's contemporaries, in turn, did likewise, followed by other interested skippers, so that eventually a considerable amount of money was riding on either contestant.

The day of the contest on the *Dawn Hunter* was one of complete misery for Sandy. He was allocated one orange and a mug of tea for breakfast while the others dined regally in the customary manner. His severe hunger pangs were minimally assuaged in mid-afternoon when the cook provided a lightly boiled egg and one slice of toast with the merest scraping of butter.

About to launch a frenzied attack on the meagre fare, Cameron advised him: "Take yer time, take yer time. There's a loat o' eatin' in an egg ye know. Take a wee, wee bit o' egg, a big, big bit o' breed an' a grett big drink o' tea. Then dae the same again. Ye'll be quite satisfied if ye dae it that way."

However, ten seconds later a few crumbs and an empty shell were all that remained on the mate's plate.

Sandy was guarded remorselessly by Cameron and Angus, especially in the vicinity of the galley, and he was a happy man when Wullie announced the commencement of hauling operations at the end of the last tow.

Steaming for Craighouse, Sandy was standing on deck gutting haddock when he announced: "Ah'm weak wae hunger. Ah'm tellin' ye, ah'm that hungry ah could eat the heid off this haddie."

Wullie calmed his mate by reminding him of the veritable feast that lay ahead.

"Jeest think, Sandy, o' aal them tatties wae a dose o' real ferm butter an' glesses o' mulk straight oot o' the coo. An' if ah know the Jura folk there'll be hunners o' scones an' cakes an' pastries efterwards at the ceilidh."

"Aw Wullie, can ye naw make the boat go any faster?" was the mate's tortured reply.

It seemed that the entire island population had turned out for the occasion. The centre of the village hall floor was taken up by four card tables placed end to end and laid with a magnificent white linen tablecloth which Lachie had scrounged from the hotel. Another table as Wullie had rightly predicted, buckled under the weight of heaps of home baking and savouries and an unofficial bar had been set up, stocked with a wide variety of drinks contributed by all present.

Clouds of steam escaped from the hall kitchen as four pans of potatoes, especially selected for uniformity, boiled in readiness for the start of the contest. Lachie welcomed Wullie and his crew. Cameron, as always on the lookout for a favourable response by a young lady, had washed, shaved and sprayed himself liberally with what he described as "foo-foo juice," a pleasant smelling deodorant. "Good to see you boys. That's big Davy over there," said Lachie indicating a man mountain that stood head and shoulders above a knot of islanders in a corner of the hall.

Apprehension overwhelmed Sandy when he caught sight of his opponent. "In the name o' Scotland. Ah know ah'm hungry but that berr could eat two o' me fur his brekkfast," he said.

Sharing Sandy's opinion regarding the obviously formidable digestive capabilities of Davy Munro, Cameron removed himself from the hall and dashed to the nearby shop, which was on the point of closing. The MacPherson charm was turned on fully towards the lovely young assistant and when Cameron asked for a certain bottle from the pharmaceutical shelf, the blushing maiden handed it over with a knowing island look and a coy smile. Promising to be her escort at the dance later, the intrepid engineer returned to the hall, where he told his shipmates: "Ah'm jeest gaan tae have a word wae the big fella tae wish him luck."

"Urr ye for a can o' beer afore ye start?" he offered the giant.

"No, no, it would blow me out terrible. But I'm thinkin' I could manage a gless o' rum an' Coke," said Davy.

Cameron came back from the makeshift bar and thrust a generous measure of Davy's pleasure into his hand. Licking his lips after downing the drink in one go, he commented: "That's funny, there's a kind o' droll taste off that rum."

"It's maybe naw yer usual brand," suggested Cameron.

Ten minutes later Lachie announced that the potatoes were ready and asked the contestants to take their places at the table. Two steaming bowls of potatoes appeared from the kitchen and, stipulating a time limit of 20 minutes, the Jura man officially started the contest.

Sandy, by this time sorely stricken with hunger, took six potatoes from the bowl in front of him and mashed them finely, adding butter and milk. The process was repeated 30 seconds later.

"Easy noo, Sandy. Take yer time, take yer time. Ye know yer the best at this kind o' gemme," cajoled Wullie, fearing that the mate would rush things too much.

At the other end of the table Davy was employing different tactics by eating one at a time, to vociferous encouragement from his fellow islanders. However, after about a dozen, the big man began to slow down and, to everyone's astonishment, had managed to eat a total of only 18 when the 20 minutes were up.

Sandy had finished his fifth batch of six when the gong sounded and declared he could have eaten more.

"But ah'm keepin' room for that big cream sponge ower there," he explained pointing to the goodies table.

"I chust don't know what iss wrong with me at all," Davy said to a dejected Lachie who was going to have to lay out a lot of money on his betting losses.

As the *Dawn Hunter*'s crew prepared to turn in much later that night following a most enjoyable ceilidh and dance, Wullie remarked to Cameron: "Ah really thought that big fella wid have had the batin' o' oor Sandy."

"So did I, but hoot dae ye think gave big Davy's rum the droll taste?" answered the engineer as he placed a little bottle on the cabin table and rolled into his bunk.

Wullie found on close examination that it contained a proprietary brand of a quick-acting slimming aid, a small dose of which was guaranteed to dull the appetite in minutes.

"Oh, dearie, dearie me. Ah hope yon big man doesna find oot aboot this. The least said the better," muttered Wullie as he turned out the light.

YARNING TIME

The *Dawn Hunter* was riding out a ferocious mid-February storm at the Isle of Gigha anchorage, where a south-easterly gale had been blowing relentlessly for 24 hours. The wind showed no signs of abating as it tore at the radio antennae in a whistling fury that caused the flakes of a driving snow shower to build up on the boat's deck and superstructure, giving her a ghostly appearance in the dark night. Below decks, the crewmen were secure in the knowledge that their anchor had a firm grip of the seabed and they sat around the cabin table in front of a magnificent coal fire. Fed and watered, they would normally have settled down to watch the portable colour television set but the storm had caused damage to the mainland transmitter that served the area resulting in a loss of picture.

Angus, who was brought up in an age of high-tech computer games and other leisure time electronic wizardry, grumbled at the lack of on-tap entertainment and intimated that he was bored.

"Ah canna even get a waalk ashore tae look at the sheep," he lamented.

"Ewes is aboot yer limit as far as weemin is concerned anyway," sniggered Cameron.

Wullie mentally spanned his fishing career of 32 years and was in reminiscent mood.

"There wis nae televeesions on boats when ah went tae the job first. When we wur at the north at the ring nettin' in the wunter we would sometimes be lying at anchor in Northbay for a week at a time. Aye, the Barra wunters wis severe in them dehs. Nights laik this wis spent yarnin' aboot anythin' an' ivverythin'."

Cameron groaned inwardly at the prospect of Wullie recounting old stories that he had heard so often and wished it were bedtime.

However, the spectral atmosphere prevalent that night must have diverted Wullie's train of thought from the stock of well-worn tales he usually fell back on during such occasions; stories that were prone to exaggeration each time they were told.

"Did ah ivver tell youse aboot the time ah saw the ghost ootside the cemetery in Cam'eltoon?" he asked Cameron, who responded with interest since he had never before heard his skipper mention such an incident.

"Well, it wis a night jeest laik this. Ah wisna lang through mah drivin' test an' ah wis giein' mah cousin a wee haan' with his taxi business at the weekends. There wis a grett big tanker in at the NATO jetty an' we wis daein' fine business aalthegither wae the sellors comin' an' gaan. Anyweh, ah wis gaan doon tae the jetty empty tae collect a ferr an' wis jeest passin' the graveyerd when a piper in fuhll Heilan' dress stepped oot on tae the rodd an' asked me hoot the time wis.

"Ah looked at the wee clock on the car's dashboard an' telt him it wis ten tae twelve. He said he wis gaan tae be late for an appointment an' ah wisna tae tell anyboady that ah had saw him.

"Ah puck up the sellor an' ah wis that bothered aboot the piper that ah telt him aboot hoot had heppened but when we passed the cemetery gates on the way back tae the toon there wis nae sign o' him.

"Ah had tae go past the place half an hoor efter that wae merr passengers on and there wis naethin' there that time but when ah wis drivin' back maself he jumped oot in front o' the car an' ah had tae slam on the brekks.

"Wullie 'Clane," he said tae me, "I telt ye naw tae tell a sowell that you saw me an' ye did."

"Wae that he turned and waalked clean through the cemetery waall.

"Ah wis shakin' that bad aboot the way he knew my name that ah had tae go straight hame fur a gless o' whusky. Ah've aye been worried that somethin' wis gaan tae heppen tae me but, touch wud, naethin' hase yit."

If anything, the wind had increased in strength and Angus's teenage imagination was running riot, causing his spine to tingle and the hairs on the back of his neck to stand up. Even Cameron half-believed Wullie's story but tested the skipper by asking; "Urr ye sure ye dinna jeest imagine seein' the piper gaan through the waall?"

"Cameron, my eyes urr as good as any man's. Anyhow, hoot wid ah waant tae make up a yarn laik that for, us being that supersteetious?"

"How urr youse so supersteetious anyweh?" questioned Angus.

"Because o' oor fethers an' their fethers afore them. You naw comin' fae fushin' stock will naw jeest understaan' right aboot it Angus," replied Wullie.

Angus was, though, beginning to understand most of the fishermen's' beliefs, thanks to regular rebukes by Sandy, administered when the cook inadvertently referred to certain rodents and furry animals by name rather than the prescribed alias.

Sandy had also told him off in his early days as a crewman for talking to a ginger-haired girl on the quay immediately prior to sailing one evening to the herring fishing.

"Nivver, ivver, speak tae a rudd-heidded wumman on yer way tae the boat," he warned.

Questioning Sandy on the origins of that particular superstition, Angus was told: "Well, A'm buggered if Ah know right, but jeest don't dae it."

That night at anchor, Angus was in persistent mood and he asked Wullie to qualify the theory of superstition by quoting examples.

"Och, there are hunners, son, but ah'll tell ye o' a couple that come tae mah mind ee noo.

"A scatter o' years ago we wurr perr-traalin' in the deep watter for white fush wae the *Silver Reaper*. The boats wis quite close thegither an' ah tweeged a dooker landin' on her stern. Noo, dookers is fine burds in their natural element but och, och, the very duvvle himself is in them if they come aboard a boat. I telt the *Silver Reaper's* skipper, Jock McSporran, aboot it on the wireless an' he ran oot the wheeluss laik a man possessed. He took a swing at the dooker wae his boot but it flew aweh afore Jock could connect an' he slipped an' fell clean on his erse. Anyweh, when we heaved up the gear the net wis toarn tae bits an' there wis nae fush in it. We wurna anywhere near bad grunn an' we didna feel the net catchin' on an obstruction on the bottom."

"But how can ye blame a poor wee burd for gettin' a bad teerin'?" asked Angus. "There wis nae other reason for it. It wis definitely the dooker an' it wis jeest oor misfortune that it decided tae visit us that deh," was Wullie's firm reply.

"Aye, an' we wis mendin' that net in the freezin' cowld an' renn fur two dehs," said Cameron as he made his way through the dividing door between the cabin and the engine room.

Wullie continued: "Another time we wis perr-traalin' at the herrin' an' Jock wis oor neebor boat. Well, we hadna got as much as a herrin' tail on the boat by the Wednesdeh an' things wis lookin' very bleak. The weather wis that bad we had to go up the River Clyde intae quieter watters. We wis makin' for Loch Long, jeest passin' Inellan, when ah minded o' a trick mah owld gran'fether telt me aboot when I wis only a wee boy.

"It wis Halloween week an' in them dehs, the owld men used tae take a lighted paper doon intae the howld tae chase aweh the evil spurits that wis surely lurkin' in the corners. Anyweh, ah got two pages oot o' the Herald, for it's a fine big paper, went doon intae the fush room an' putt a match tae them.

"Ah shook them aal ower the place an' the boys thought ah wis clean droll, tryin' tae putt the boat on fire for the insurance. But they wurna laughin' when we shot in Loch Long an' got two hunner units o' grett big herrin'."

At this juncture a head with a most grotesque countenance appeared through the cabin door and an eerie voice droned: "I am the ghost o' Wullie Clane's grandfether. Ye'll need tae light merr papers tae putt aweh this gale o' wund."

Wullie and Sandy both gave a start but the apparition had considerably more effect on the cook; with the gale screaming above his head, Angus was petrified.

A vestige of calm was restored shortly afterwards when the mask was removed to reveal Cameron's broad grin. He explained that he had bought the mask months before to protect his face from stinging jellyfish at the herring fishing and it had lain forgotten in an engine room locker. He had remembered about it when Wullie mentioned Halloween.

"Aw, can youse naw speak aboot somethin' else," begged Angus.

"Well, come on then, gie us wan o' yer ain yarns tae pass the time," Sandy suggested to the cook.

"Och, how am ah supposed tae know the stories laik youse owld fellas. Sure ah'm naw that lang oot the school," replied Angus.

"Hoot aboot the time we went tae the exhibeetion Angus?" Cameron enquired. The engineer's question embarrassed Angus visibly.

"Ah thought you said you winna tell anybody aboot that Cameron. That's naw ferr."

Wullie and Sandy, interest aroused, demanded the details.

The occasion in question was the annual Scottish Fishermans' Exhibition — an event held in Glasgow, and well patronised by fishermen from all over the country. Angus and his teenage mate, Johnny Grant, travelled to the city with Cameron for a two-day visit, though Wullie and Sandy missed the affair due to prior commitments.

Cameron took up the story: "We went tae the exhibeetion in the moarnin' an' had a braw terr. Efter dinnertime we thought we would go an' see a fulm that was showin' at the Odeon but Johnny wis waantin' somethin' oot o' a shop in Argyle Street so we said we would meet him at the dorr o' the picture hoose.

"We wis stannin' wettin' for him for donkeys an oor Angus here wis gettin' the wund up tae some tune in case we wid miss the film.

"Anyweh, he went ower tae the lassie that wis sellin' the tickets an' asked her if Johnny Grant wis aweh in yet. Did ye ivver hear o' anythin' merr Heilan' than that? Imagine askin' a wumman in the middle o' Glesca if she'd sold his mate a ticket. As if she wid know Johnny Grant.

"An' if that wisna bad enough we went tae Marks an' Spencer efter the pictures an' the bowld Angus telt waan o' the weemin at the checkoots that she wid be aawful busy because there wis a bus trip up fae Cam'eltoon that deh!"

"Och, ah wisna thinkin' right Cameron," Angus tried to explain amid hoots of laughter from the skipper and the mate.

"Ye wisna thinkin' right later on that night either wae aal that vodka an' lime ye wur drinkin'. Mind you, the crack ye made tae thon heid waiter wis a good yin," continued Cameron.

He went on to tell how Angus, Johnny and himself, decided to treat themselves by dining in an up-market city centre eating establishment. By pure coincidence, a group of young fishermen known to them occupied a nearby table and it soon became apparent that they were giving the waiting staff a hard time. More than once, dishes were taken back to the kitchen for replacement, although it appeared that the food was cooked to a high standard. Their general attitude was one of haughtiness. Wine, too, was rejected because the bouquet was not to their liking.

"Youse should have heard them," said Cameron. "Ye wid think they wur brought up in Blenheim Palace an' went tae the school at Eton. It's young yuppie fushermen laik them that gies us a bad name. They were naethin' but a bunch o' upstarts."

He told how the three Campbeltown men savoured an expensive but thoroughly enjoyable dinner and Angus was detailed to pay the bill. As he was doing so he overheard one of the *upstarts* complaining to a waiter that the toilets needed cleaning, a claim which Angus knew to be untrue since he had paid a visit to the gents only minutes previously.

Handing the head waiter a £5 tip, Angus made reference to the portable fishing boat toilets that are fashioned from discarded five-gallon oil containers and he remarked loudly: "See them that's givin' ye aal the hassle, you'd nivver think they spent aal week shittin' in owld oil drums, wid ye?"

"Good on ye, Angus, that wid haive putt them in their place right enough," said Wullie.

"Speakin' aboot restaurants," began Sandy, ah must tell youse aboot the time ah packed in my berth on the *Ocean Searcher.*"

Sandy described how, as a 16-year-old newly liberated from Campbeltown Grammar School, he had secured a job as cook on the 40-foot vessel. After only a few days aboard the boat and during which time he was subjected to some fairly severe *before the mast* treatment, Sandy decided that the skipper, Hughie Scott, was nothing but a tyrant.

Hughie also fancied himself, wrongly, as a top-flight skipper and frequently doubled the size of his catch when reporting trawling results to other skippers on the radio.

"Aye, he wis a helluva man right enough," Sandy went on.

"Ah mind wan o' the other crewmen, Jeck Wilson, tellin' me that Hughie wis spoutin' off in the Clachan Bar wan Setturdeh night aboot aal the money he wis makin' at the fushin'. He had a good drink in him an' he dinna notice Jeck stannin' at the bar. When he told aal hands he had settled two hunner an' eighty poun' wages that moarnin' Jeck tapped him on the shooder an' said he must have been on a half sherr that week. Seemin'ly Hughie wis clean black affrontit. "Anyweh, ah had tae stick it aboard the *Ocean Searcher* for merr than two years because dacent berths were as scarce as rockin' horses' shit. Wan Setterdeh ah got word o' a good job an' jumped at the chance. Ah wis in fine trum an' me an' a couple o' mates decided tae haive a bar lunch in wan o' the hotels."

Sandy told how, on entering the premises, they noticed Hughie sitting at a table with several relatives who were on holiday from Glasgow. Hughie spied the youths and he sauntered across to their table.

He discreetly pressed a £5 note into Sandy's hand with the instructions: "Get me a big gless o' whusky an' take it ower tae my table. Say it is for the best skipper in Cam'eltoon when ye putt it doon in front o' me."

Sandy dutifully went to the bar and ordered a weak half-pint beer shandy, took it to Hughie's table and presented the glass to his now ex-skipper with the words: "This is for the biggest bloody eediot ah'm ivver laikely tae work for. That's me feenished on your boat."

The mate concluded: "Aye, ye should have seen the look on Hughie's face when the Glesca yins started laughin' at him. Even his big baald heid wis rudd, he wis that affrontit."

The mention of a bald head spurred Cameron to recount the tale which he referred to as "Geordie's revenge".

The principle character was a fisherman called Geordie Fraser. Geordie was almost hairless and on the wrong side of 40, and, although he was unfortunately never destined to rival Adonis in the good looks league, he nevertheless pursued the ladies almost relentlessly. He was quite undeterred by the total rejection he received and he became the target of some cruelly witty jibes from certain quarters.

Geordie liked to keep what little hair he had left in a neat and tidy fashion and was a regular visitor to a local hairdressing salon. There, also, he was the butt of jokes aimed by both hairdresser and customers alike.

Cameron recalled how, on one occasion, Geordie happened to mention in the shop that he was going to Italy on holiday in the very near future. The barber, well aware that Geordie was a devout Roman Catholic, shifted tack from the usual subject of his lack of success with women. Instead, he asked Geordie if he was likely to be in Rome and, if so, would he perhaps try and meet the Pope. Geordie's answer in the affirmative was met with sniggers from the assembled company.

Cameron happened to be in the hairdresser's shop some weeks later when Geordie, newly returned from his vacation, called in. The barber pounced immediately and loudly demanded to know if he had made it to Rome.

"Aye, ah wis in Rome."

"And did you meet His Holiness?" the hairdresser probed further.

"Aye," came the gruff reply.

"And what did he say to you Geordie?"

"He asked me who gave me the terrible lookin' herrcut."

The eruption of laughter in the shop was probably equalled that night in the *Dawn Hunter*'s cabin.

Wullie concluded the evening's yarns with a story from his own youth, evoked by his cook's earlier frustration at having no television to watch.

"It wis in the dehs o' Radio Luxembourg an' Radio Caroline. Och aye, the very heydeh o' the sixties when we aal had long herr an' went aboot in Beatle jeckets an' winkle picker shoes.

"Oor crew on the *Welcome Home* wis aal young except for owld Hector MacKay the skipper who wis due for retirin' any time.

"Anyweh, we managed tae get the big Coastal wireless on the boat tuned in tae Radio Caroline wan deh an' we asked Hector if he wad get us an extension speaker so that we could hear it oot on the dake.

"Noo, owld Hector wis hellish foand o' a dram when his work wis feenished an' he went ashore ivvery night nae matter wherr we wur lyin'. That night we tied up at Brodick an' Hector, true tae form, climbed on tae the pier and disappeared aweh up the village.

"We wis aal turned in an' sleepin' sound when he roared doon the hatch that he waanted us tae get up an' gie him a haan' wae somethin'. It turned oot he had a good dram in him an' he had swaapped an owld spare net fur a set o' bagpipes wae a Brodick fella he knew.

"When the net wis haauled on tae the quay an' we made tae go back tae wir beds Hector wad have nane o' it.

"Youse wanted music and it is music youse'll get."

"Noo, Hector might have been a dammnt good fusherman but he wis aawful bad at the pipin'. He started plehin' slow Gaelic airs an' laments doon in the foreccassel and I'm tellin' youse, the noise wis that bad oor eardrums wur near burstin'.

"Thankfully, at aboot wan o'clock in the moarnin' a big polisman came doon aboard an waarned Hector if he dinna stop the racket at wance he was fur liftin'

him for breach o' the peace. Seemin'ly the haalf o' Brodick wis wakened wae the row.

"Aye, that wis the end o' Radio Caroline on the *Welcome Home*."

The crew of the *Dawn Hunter* made ready for bed and Angus stoked up the fire as the wind roared in the stove chimney. He thought about the evening gone by - time which had passed all too quickly, and he realised that there was, indeed, more to life that video games, compact disc players and elaborate fruit machines.

WULLIE'S POUND COIN CON

Perfect harmony prevailed on the *Dawn Hunter*, and all hands were in particularly good spirits. The reason was simple; they were participating in the annual queen scallops - known locally as crechans - fishery in Kilbrannan Sound. Trawling in shallow water, the boat was sometimes only a hundred yards or so from the Kintyre shore as she followed the eight fathoms contour line a few miles north of Campbeltown, which meant that she seldom left an even keel in even the stiffest of westerly breezes. The duration of the hauls were short, making the work more interesting and the day seemed to pass quickly.

Wullie and the lads had just spent a harrowing three weeks fishing for prawns during a prolonged spell of bad weather on the grounds south-west of Ailsa Craig, in the southern approaches to the Firth of Clyde, and the smoother waters of the Sound were a most welcome diversion.

Fishing was good and the superior quality of the crechans meant excellent prices followed by good wages. It was now September and Wullie hoped that, with luck, the fishery would last until mid-November, when the sprat shoals normally showed up.

Lingering over a late breakfast in the mess deck while Sandy had temporary command, Wullie picked up the previous day's newspaper. Scanning the columns, his eyes were suddenly riveted to a news story update on a security van hijack, which had taken place in Glasgow a week previously.

According to the report, the city police had picked up information suggesting that the £100,000 haul of £1 coins and high value used notes had been taken from Glasgow by boat and jettisoned at a designated spot on the seabed somewhere in the Firth of Clyde, to be recovered later when the *heat* was off.

When he had finished reading the article aloud to Angus and Cameron, Wullie commented on the possibility of a Clyde fishing vessel accidentally turning up the hoard, only to be met with light-hearted derisory reaction from his subordinates. "Stranger things haive heppened in the coorse o' a deh," commented the skipper enigmatically as he rose from the table to relieve the mate in the wheelhouse.

Sandy, whom Cameron once said would "sell his ain granny for a shullin'," showed extreme interest in the latest developments of the hijacking as he tackled his usual gargantuan fry-up with enthusiasm.

Back in the wheelhouse, skipper William Andrew Maclean decided he was going to have a *terr* with his crew on the subject of the stolen cash.

The skipper liked to go out on deck at the end of each haul to examine the quantity and quality of the shells. Whilst the others were involved in securing the lifting tackle safely in place, Wullie tied the special slipknot on the codend. With his back to the crew he pushed a small round object, taken from a special emergency kitty, into the pile of crechans before returning to the wheelhouse. Crechans are landed in sacks and the quickest method of handling them is to shovel them straight off the deck into bags. The *Dawn Hunter*'s crew took turns at shovelling or holding the bags open and it was Angus, wielding a No 10 roadman's shovel, who suddenly stopped and picked out a shining £1 coin from the heap.

"In the name o' the wee man, wherr the duvvle did this come fae?" he exclaimed.

"Ach, it laikley enough fell off a yat," was Cameron's explanation.

"Well, it's finder's keepers," stated the cook as he slipped the coin into his boiler suit pocket; Sandy looked on in anguish.

During the next few hours the *Dawn Hunter*'s crew uncovered a total of nine £1 coins from the trawled up crechans, and the situation prompted serious discussion between Sandy, Cameron and Angus.

"Dae ye think fur wan meenute it could be the money missin' fae Glesca?" asked Angus.

"Ah don't know. But there must be thoosands o' them doon there if we're liftin' them wae this gear," reasoned Sandy.

The mate continued: "Don't say waan word tae Wullie. He's got a dose o' money an' a grett big hoose as weel," which was the precise reaction the skipper had hoped for.

As the day's fishing drew to a close, Wullie announced that since the creachans were thinning out somewhat, they would be trying a different patch the next day. This sparked off an intense study of the shoreland and hills beyond by Cameron and Sandy. They were not enraptured by the stunning natural beauty of the area, but were pinpointing the boat's exact position by using landmarks such as trees, fields, dykes and cottages.

Easing his head and shoulders out of a wheelhouse window, Wullie, fully aware of what the other two were doing, let his gaze wander shoreward as he surveyed the scenery. Sparkling wavelets broke quietly on to a shore of almost pure white sand, which gave way to fields of lush pasture. The rolling meadows were met by high hills carpeted with sturdy, erect evergreens that brushed the blue skyline.

"Aye, aye boys, it's God's ain country, is it naw? The land o' mulk an' honey right enough," observed Wullie.

"Ach, we wis jeest watchin' a coo tryin' tae get aweh fae a grett big buhll," Cameron retorted.

With the crew's full attention centred aft whilst heaving the heavy trawl aboard at the completion of the last haul, Wullie sidled out on deck. Unseen, he prepared and dropped over the side two huge canvas bags he had unearthed from the boat's forepeak store, along with a further four £1 coins.

The remainder of the week's fishing was carried out without incident off the Arran shore and it was a happy skipper who settled wages of £320 per man on Friday evening.

Handing the envelopes round, Wullie bade his crew the customary good wishes for the weekend and made his way home.

Low water at Campbeltown on Saturday morning was predicted for 09.27, and Sandy, Cameron and Angus arranged to meet on the pier at 08.30 at the point where the mate's dory was moored. The plan, hatched in the early evening quiet of the Feathers Inn lounge bar, was simple. Sandy would dive the few fathoms to what must surely be the loot from the Glasgow robbery. Angus and Cameron would haul it to the surface, whereupon the threesome would divide it.

Pangs of guilt began to penetrate Angus's enthusiasm for the project. Brought up in a strict Presbyterian household, he still attended church each Sunday and honesty was held as an important value within his family.

"Can we naw jeest tell the polis wherr it is. Ah suppose there'll be a good reward," he pleaded.

Sandy almost choked on his lager and spluttered: "Don't be ridiculous, we'll dae nae such thing. There's naethin' officially tae suggest that the money came fae Glesca. Anyweh, the security crowd wull be well-insured fur the laiks o' this. An' forbye, ah thought you wur waantin' a new motor bike."

Thus placated, Angus was once more in total agreement with the others.

The morning dawned to reveal ideal diving conditions with a cloudless blue sky accompanied by nothing more than a whisper of wind which hardly ruffled a flat calm sea. The three brigands set off from Campbeltown as unobtrusively as possible and the 16-foot dinghy slowed down at the exact location some 40 minutes later, thanks to the meticulous land bearings taken by Sandy and Cameron the previous day.

Their departure, however, had not gone unnoticed by Wullie in his *grett big hoose* standing on the hillside overlooking the quay. He and a friend left the town by car shortly afterwards and arrived at the spot at the same time. Wullie parked his big estate car out of sight behind a rocky outcrop just off the main road and they took up positions completely hidden from the three mariners.

Meanwhile, the dory was the scene of feverish activity. Angus assisted Sandy into his diving suit and accessories as Cameron kept the boat on station. Five minutes later the *Dawn Hunter*'s mate slipped over the side and descended to the bottom, where visibility was good. A thin nylon line, being paid out by Angus, snaked out behind him from his weighted belt.

After a brief reconnaissance of the seabed, Sandy had to concentrate hard on controlling the regularity of his breathing. The worshipper of Midas had spied the two bags and the few coins lying on the ocean floor and a quick examination convinced him he had found the proceeds of the Glasgow hijacking.

His heart beat like an enthusiastic rock band's bass drum as he told himself: "Ah've cracked it this wan time. Ah'll nivver be poor again wae aal that lovely dough."

Sandy attached the nylon rope securely to the first bag with a round turn and two half hitches. Two sharp tugs on the line was the signal for Cameron and Angus to begin hauling and the dory heeled crazily as they took the strain. Inch by laborious inch they heaved until at last the bag.broke the surface. A Herculean effort was required to unceremoniously ship it inboard.

Cameron attached an old shackle to the end of the rope for weight and it was lowered once again to the submerged Sandy. Seconds later a further two sharp tugs on the line told them there was another bag on the way up.

This time Sandy's head popped up before the bag and, removing his breathing apparatus, he shouted excitedly: "Ah telt youse. ah'm nivver wrang when it comes tae money metters. I might even spen' some o' it."

The other bag was duly taken aboard, followed by the ecstatic Sandy. With his big diving knife he gingerly sliced into the canvas material, expecting to see a jackpot of coins spill out like confetti. The three shipmates looked at one another in mute and uncomprehending silence as the gash revealed not a fortune, but a bag stuffed with old heavy chandlery, chain and a 56lb weight. The second bag surrendered similar contents and a slim oilskin-wrapped package. On opening it was found to contain a piece of stiff cardboard on which was emblazoned in large capitals EVER BEEN HAD?

Wullie's friend, Eric Hunter, using a sophisticated camera fitted with a powerful telephoto lens recorded in detail the ensuing pantomime aboard the dory.

Eric, the local newspaper's photographer, shared Wullie's keen sense of humour and he laughed heartily as he shot off a 24-exposure film at rapid speed.

Sandy all but capsized the boat when he hurled the bags and scrap back into the water in a fit of unadulterated fury. Cameron and Angus argued hotly before the cook transferred his wrath to Sandy.

"Ye might be able tae smell money a mile away, but it's a helluva peety ye canna smell bullshit," he shouted at the mate who now sat in the stern, head in hands. "Aye,"said Cameron, "there wis as much chance o' findin' herrin' at the top o' Ben Ghulean as there wis o' turnin' up a fortune here."

"Ah wis that sure o' it," was the mate's meek response.

Cameron, so often the instigator of practical jokes, found it particularly hard to accept the fact that for once he had been well and truly conned in that he had fallen victim to an elaborately planned and superbly executed hoax; but by whom?

The disenchanted trio disembarked quietly at Campbeltown and made their way up the Old Quay, Sandy having surreptitiously slipped the four coins into his pocket. They said goodbye with barely audible grunts.

Wullie and Eric were by this time in the latter's darkroom, where the development of the film was taking place. The *Dawn Hunter's* skipper intended to exploit his crew's misfortune to the limit and the successful printing of the photographs delighted him.

Marvelling at the composition and clarity of each one, he told the pressman: "Aye, yer cluvver at yer job right enough, Eric. Ye'll get a damned good refreshment for this."

The penultimate stage in Wullie's inspired *terr* took place in the newspaper's pressroom, where Eric and a printer friend roped into the ploy produced a mock front page. A banner headline, set above a big picture of the three heroes closely examining a 56lb weight, proclaimed: LOCAL FISHERMEN RECOVER SUNKEN TREASURE! and the accompanying story ridiculed them mercilessly.

In the evening, Wullie made his way to Cameron's favourite watering hole, a combined lounge bar/discotheque that the young set of the town patronised. He was gratified to witness increasing numbers of *with it* revellers arrive on the premises despite having to suffer an intense attack on his eardrums by the resident disc jockey's high decibel offerings.

Cameron and three friends eventually arrived and, on observing his skipper sitting on a bar stool, approached him with the query: "Hoot's an owld man laik you daein' in here. Does the wife an' weans know yer oot?"

Raucous laughter from the four young bloods followed the question.

Wullie was quite unperturbed and accepted a double whisky from his engineer with the enquiry: "Hoot wur ye up tae the deh Cameron?"

A slight pause was followed by: "Ach, ye know me Wullie. Ah had a terr wae my mates here; jeest the usual."

"Aye, aye, ah had a bit o' a terr maself," answered Wullie casting a long and meaningful look at the pub's notice board, where half a dozen young ladies were highly amused as they studied the pinned up newspaper page.

Two minutes later, the clown prince of the Campbeltown fleet was back at the bar in a state of embarrassed agitation. He wished his skipper good health with the words: "See that drink, ah hope it chokes ye. An' ah hope yur next shite's a hedgehog."

Wullie downed his whisky with no ill effects, wished Cameron an affable goodnight and escaped to the sanity of the Feathers, where his contemporaries were regaled with a wonderful yarn.

HIGH JINKS IN OBAN

The *Dawn Hunter* was ploughing her ponderous way through a head-on north-easterly gale which sent sheets of spray flying high above her decks as she reared and plunged into the motion. The strong sunlight's reflection on the thousands of airborne water particles gave the impression that the boat was being bombarded by countless tiny silver darts.

She was making for Oban, via the Sound of Mull, from the fishing grounds surrounding Skerryvore Lighthouse, south of Tiree, after a successful three-day trip for valuable fish such as hake, haddock, plaice and sole. Progress was slow owing to the adverse weather conditions and the effects of a strong ebb tide running in the same direction as the sea.

"Och, it's at times laik this that ah wush ah had a sweetie shop," complained Wullie as he nursed his beloved vessel through another huge trough.

"Ah don't think we're ivver gaan tae get past Tiree," he added

"If ah had a pound for ivvery time ah heard you chitterin' aboot a sweetie shop ah winna be stannin' here. It's the Bahamas ah wid be in," answered Cameron, who was on watch with the skipper while Angus and Sandy rested below.

Ignoring his engineer's sardonic reply, Wullie went on: "Ah don't know how that perr doon in the cebin can sleep through this. Ah believe they could doss on the edge o' a razor blade."

Despite his frequent threats to set himself up as a confectioner and his vituperative condemnations of the sea, Wullie had no intention of giving up his calling. Though he much preferred working closer to home in the Sound of Jura or Firth of Clyde, the astute business side of his nature sometimes led him to waters much further afield and, consequently, more turbulent. This was one such occasion and it had paid off handsomely despite having been caught in the gale. For his boat's fishroom held a rich bounty of 187 fifty-kilogram boxes of eminently marketable fish gleaned from an ocean which, until only a few hours ago, had been in a rare state of serenity for the previous three days.

Wullie's skilful reading of his comprehensive range of electronic underwater detection equipment on a largely unfished stony seabed had led to the bumper catch. By using a robust *rockhopper* trawl, damage to the gear had been minimal on the rough grounds.

Four hours later the *Dawn Hunter* reached the sanctuary of the Sound of Mull. Passing close to Rubha nan Gall Lighthouse, on the west side of Tobermory, Wullie told Cameron to call out Angus and Sandy to take over the watch for the passage down the calmer waters of the sound. This would take longer than usual for the tide had now turned and they were boring an equally strong floodwater running up the sound.

Rubbing the sleep from his eyes as he turned out of his bunk, Sandy announced: "Och, ah dinna get a bloody wink at aal. Ah saw ivvery 'oor on the clock."

The engineer knew only too well that Sandy's statement meant that he had been asleep for at least five of the six hours he had been below. Unless the mate had eight uninterrupted hours he invariably complained that he "couldna get aweh at aal."

There were no such comments from Angus, who had to be shaken three times before making a bleary-eyed exit from his bunk.

Wullie and Cameron spent the next few hours in oblivion until Angus advised them that the boat was approaching the Island of Kerrera, which stands sentinel at the entrance to Oban Bay.

This was the vessel's first landing in Oban for some time and it was a visit anticipated with relish by Cameron and Angus. It was early September and the popular holiday resort was still buzzing with tourists, and that meant a plentiful supply of girls to ply with seafaring charm, welcome or otherwise. According to Cameron, though, Angus's chat-up lines were nothing more than "verbal diarrhoea" and he still had a lot to learn when it came to the art of wooing the fairer sex.

Approaching Oban's North Pier, Cameron was pleased to note the presence of a huge banner strung along the esplanade railings indicating that the town was playing host to a big music festival. It was Thursday evening and, with a strong north-easterly breeze still blowing, there was a good chance they would be detained in port until it eased somewhat.

A lorry ordered earlier by Wullie using his mobile telephone was waiting on the pier to be loaded with the catch for transportation to the Aberdeen fish market, where prices were reported to be excellent. The landing derrick and necessary ropes were made ready and discharging operations commenced, closely witnessed by the ubiquitous flock of squawking seagulls, ever watchful in the hope of picking up a morsel or two.

Calamity struck midway through the unloading of the catch when the hydraulically operated cargo winch hissed to a halt. A quick examination of the hydraulic pipes by Cameron revealed nothing and it was obvious that the problem was of a more serious nature. Twenty minutes later it was established that the main pump supplying the boat's hydraulics with the necessary fluid had suffered a major malfunction and was unable to maintain the required pressure in the pipes.

The problem of discharging 90 boxes remaining in the hold was solved by Wullie, who arranged for a local boat to come alongside and, using a series of blocks and ropes, the fish was heaved ashore by the other vessel's winch.

An hour of frenzied telephoning from the fishsalesman's office resulted in the news that a replacement pump could not be in Oban until Monday at the earliest.

Wullie contacted his wife with a request that she drive to Oban to collect the crew and the *Dawn Hunter* was moored alongside a huge herring purse-seiner at the Railway Pier.

The prospect of a long weekend in Oban pleased Cameron immensely and he told Wullie he would remain on board.

"Pumps is my deperrtment an' ah'll need tae be here when it arrives," he said.

"Ah'll jeest wett as well. Ah wis waantin' tae gie the cebin an' gelley a spring clean anyhow," Angus added quickly.

"September's a droll time tae be spring cleanin'," observed Wullie with a knowing chuckle.

Two hours later the *Dawn Hunter*'s carefree bachelors waved goodbye to Wullie's car as it swept off the Railway Pier and headed for Campbeltown.

It was nearly bedtime when Cameron and Angus retired to the mess deck for a final cup of tea and a discussion on the delights of the coming weekend. A few minutes later Cameron realised with terrible certainty that there was going to be a major obstacle in their path - the lack of cash.

"Och, surely Wullie wid lee' us a scatter o' poun'," said Angus as he feverishly searched places in the galley which the skipper had used previously when dispensing unofficial payments to the crew.

The failure to turn up even the smallest amount left Angus truly despondent and he uttered: "Hoot urr we gaan tae dae the morra? We havena a bloody sou between us."

Unknown to them, Wullie intended to ring the Oban fishsalesman first thing in the morning with instructions to make sure that his two crewmen were financially sound in the strange port. But the immediate concern aboard the *Dawn Hunter* prompted much discussion between the shipmates before Cameron announced: "There's only wan thing for it ah'm afraid. We'll need tae fillet them podlies ah was keepin' fur Jamie Blair an' sell them tae the hotels."

He was referring to three boxes of low value small saithe, which were still in the fishroom. He had a standing arrangement with Kintyre lobsterman Jamie Blair to supply bait in return for occasional free lobsters. His intention was to pass off the saithe as haddock to unsuspecting hoteliers and restauranteurs.

"Ye canna dae that. They'll tweeg it's naw haddies an' we'll get the jyle," said Angus.

"Naw they'll naw. We'll lee them steepin' in the fush waasher aal night an' the flesh is bound tae lighten up a bit."

By 3 am Angus and Cameron had filleted the three boxes of slightly dark-coloured saithe, giving a yield of approximately 60 kilograms of fish, which was to be offered for sale at £3 per kilo.

After a few hours sleep and a good breakfast, Cameron said to Angus: "Right, aweh an' try that big hotel up there. They'll surely take a good puckle."

"That's naw ferr, puttin' me up there maself. How urr you naw comin' tae?" asked Angus.

"Ah'll need tae wett aboord in case maybe a tooerist waants tae buy some. Anyhow, you've got a braw honest face on ye," explained Cameron.

Angus truly excelled as a salesman and, within a couple of hours, the unlikely entrepreneurs had a healthy profit of £90 each.

Only one hotel chef was dubious about the species to which the fillets belonged but the soaking in salt water had, indeed, paled the fish considerably and this, along with Angus's earnest assurances that he was a bona fide fisherman, convinced the man.

By late morning the shipmates, Angus having conveniently forgotten about his avowed intention of scrubbing and polishing the accommodation area, were washed and clad in trendy going ashore gear and were about to disembark from the *Dawn Hunter* when a sonorous voice from the pier above the boat rang out:

"Is that yersel' Cameron MacPherson. I havena seen ye since the waar."

The voice belonged to an old friend of Cameron's, Jeck Sinclair, whom indeed he had not encountered for a long time, but hardly as far back as the '39-'45 hostilities!

"Well, well, if it's naw Jeck Sinclair. How urr ye gettin' on ye owld rascal," inquired Cameron.

Jeck explained that his boat was on the slip for repairs at Ardmaleish Boatyard, on the Isle of Bute, and he was now resident in Oban, having married a local girl who had managed to entice him from his native Tarbert, Loch Fyne.

"Are you still takin' a dram Cameron?"

"Too true, Jeck. Urr ye for the Claredon?"

Without further ado the two men made off in the direction of the nearby hotel, Angus having intimated that he wished to have a look round the shops.

As sometimes happens when two fishing acquaintances meet after a long absence, both the conversation and the whisky flowed with considerable fluency until eventually the concerned barman decided that the vociferous nature of the repartee had reached a level most annoying to other customers and he asked them quietly to leave the premises.

Probably realising through an alcoholic haze that the bartender was right, Cameron and Jeck made an exaggeratedly gracious exit from the establishment, to a round of applause from the other punters.

"Ah'll shee ye doon tae the boat, Cameron. I don't want ye to fall in the watter," Jeck offered.

The erratic progress of the two friends towards the pier was noted with interest by a number of Oban residents before they eventually arrived at the boat, only to be met with a problem. During their sojourn in the pub the tide had fallen alarmingly and Cameron was faced with a 15-foot descent on a slippery iron-runged ladder, an exercise to be treated with great caution when stone-cold sober, let alone his present condition.

Cameron spied Angus sitting on the *Dawn Hunter*'s foredeck; a very different looking Angus in fact. The cook had been the victim of an earnest haircutting operation and his shoulders were now topped by a fearfully closely shaven head, which apparently was the current fad.

"Well, ah know I'm as fuhll as a wulk, but ah wid rether be in this state as the state you're in son," said Cameron. Ah'm gaan tae caall ye the Skull o' Kintyre fae noo on. Dearie me, there urr better lookin' men lyin' doon in Kilkerran Cemetery," he added before laboriously lowering himself on to a quayside bollard where he sat and considered his predicament.

"Ye'll need tae gie me a wee haan doon aboard son. Ah wis only kiddin' ye on aboot the herrcut; honest."

The good-natured Angus appreciated that the inebriated engineer could not resist making some appropriate comment about his way-out hairdo and knew there was no malice whatever intended but he decided to silence Cameron with the reply: "Hoot urr ye sehin' man? When ye soak up aal that whusky ye lose aal yer looks. You've got a face laik a ragman's trumpet. If ah had a face laik that ah'd shave my arse an' waalk backwards."

The cook's remarks had the desired effect on the handsome prince, whose wounded pride was evident as he slid slowly off the mooring bollard and sat on the quay.

Angus, however, faced a double dilemma. Firstly, he had to get Cameron aboard the purse-seiner they were lying alongside and then across the big boat on to their own.

He decided it would be physically impossible to escort him safely down the ladder and saw only one alternative - Cameron would have to be brought aboard by mechanical means. A somewhat sheepish Angus hailed the purser's skipper and explained his predicament.

The stern-faced man reluctantly agreed to start the vessel's auxiliary engine so that the boom swinger, a derrick used to land herring, could be activated. Angus climbed on to the pier and made fast substantial rope strops around Cameron's middle and underarms before the engineer was gently lifted into the air and landed safely on the deck of the *Dawn Hunter*.

An equally po-faced knot of purser crewmen watched the proceedings with an air of quiet indifference until the skipper began to lecture Angus on the evils of strong drink. This served as a cue for the others and they chipped in with various biblical passages that condemned the use of alcohol.

It transpired that the men belonged to a close brethren sect that held rigid doctrines, including complete temperance.

Realising that his cook was on the receiving end of an unwelcome talking-to, Cameron shouted across to thank the men for taking the trouble to see him aboard without mishap and added: "Och, ah don't know hoot youse urr haverin' aboot. Sure Jesus himself turned watter intae vino collapso."

Angus reckoned that it was now time to silence his joyful shipmate and see him installed in his bunk, especially since the air was being filled with a loud and drunken version of *MacPherson's Rant*.

Five minutes later, the *Dawn Hunter*'s cabin could easily be mistaken for the scene of tree-felling operations as Cameron's snores, reminiscent of a sizeable chain saw, echoed from the bulkheads.

Angus knew it would be safe to leave his friend to sleep off the results of his chance encounter with Jeck Sinclair and, since it was now late afternoon, he decided to go ashore and have a Chinese meal. He had just climbed on to the pier when a representative of the fishsalesman's office introduced himself and handed over a brown envelope: "Your skipper has been in touch with us and has asked me to make sure you and your shipmate got this. Have a nice night."

Angus quickly established that the envelope contained £75 each for himself and Cameron and there was a spring in his step as he made his way to the Chinese restaurant, to the strains of folk and country music that drifted to his ears from the various pubs participating in the music festival.

Replete after a Cantonese feast he decided to seek out an inn which catered for the younger age group and was delighted to find upon entering the first one that the premises were being patronised by a clientele on a wave length similar to his own.

As he sipped at a pint of lager Angus took in his surroundings and something strange, indeed, happened to him. His eyes met those of a raven-haired young beauty standing with a group of friends, and when she lowered her eyelids and smiled demurely at him Angus Robertson fell hopelessly and unmistakably in love. With an absolutely Herculean show of courage the *Dawn Hunter*'s cook approached the girl and introduced himself as a Campbeltown fisherman whose boat was in Oban for repair and would not be sailing again until early in the coming week. Her name was Joy, she told him, and she lived at Salen, on the nearby Isle of Mull. She explained that a few island friends and herself were able to enjoy the night life in Oban thanks to the Caledonian MacBrayne ferry company's late night sailing to Craignure.

The next few hours passed in a blur as Angus, battling heroically to overcome his natural shyness, attempted to make conversation with Joy, despite having drunk more lager than was good for him. Joy, on the other hand, realised the anguish he was suffering and had taken a real liking to Angus and when she asked him to make the crossing to Mull the following day to see her again he was ecstatic.

He escorted Joy to the 11 pm sailing and watched the car ferry *Isle of Mull* disappear into the darkness. On returning to the *Dawn Hunter*'s cabin he was pleased to note that the forestry operations had ceased and Cameron was snoozing quietly, though he would awaken with the traditional hangover.

Early Saturday morning saw the strong north-easterly abate to a light breeze and Cameron was grateful for its soothing properties as he stood in the wheelhouse, his head protruding from a window. Angus entered bearing two mugs of strong, hot coffee and furnished full details of the purse-seiner incident to the engineer, who now wished he was anywhere but Oban, including 90 miles offshore in a gale at the Stanton Banks.

He agreed to accompany Angus to Mull, the decision being made easier when told that Joy had an older, unattached sister.

"Aweh up tae the Calmac office fur tickets an' see hoot times the boat goes at an' ah'll hae a waash an' a shave," he told the cook.

Angus strolled along the Railway Pier, impressed by the huge bulk of the car ferries *Isle of Mull* and *Clansman*, which took up a lot of berthing space. He was pleased to discover that the Mull sailings were fairly frequent and purchased the necessary tickets before rejoining his shipmate.

By midday Cameron could suffer the effects of the hangover no longer. He said: "Och, Jeck Sinclair made some job o' me yesterdeh. Come on up tae the Claredon for jeest wan or two beers tae putt me tae rights."

By shortly after three they made their way back to the Railway Pier in a condition that could be reasonably described as exuberant.

As they passed the booking office the joyous shipmates were vaguely aware of a uniformed Calmac employee engaged in earnest discussion with a group of passengers. With blithe disregard they embarked and immediately located the lounge bar, which would open on the vessel's departure.

Noticing a bulkhead clock over the rim of his pint glass about an hour and a half later, Cameron said with apprehension: "Angus, ah'm naw the world's grettest navigator, but unless Craignure's been shifted up the Soon o' Mull we're in trouble boy an' it'll naw be this day that ye'll see the Joy o' yer life."

A quick look out on deck and an equally speedy visit to the purser's office confirmed the awful truth - the two intrepid mariners were long past Craignure on board the *Clansman* bound for Castlebay, Barra in the Outer Hebrides. They were told the Mull ferry had suffered a slight technical hitch that necessitated a delay and the *Clansman* had been slipped into the embarkation berth. All would have been clear if they had stopped to listen to the Calmac official who was talking to the passengers at the booking office.

"Wherr the duvvle is Barra, anyhow?" inquired a sadly dejected Angus who had only ever heard of the island when Wullie was recalling herring fishing experiences of his youth.

Cameron replied: "Well, it's a good job we've a wheen o' poun' on us for its aboot a hunner miles oot intae the Atlantic and ye'll naw get back tae Oban this night, far less Salen."

Cameron knew that the ferry called briefly at Castlebay before going on to Lochboisdale, on South Uist, finally docking for an overnight stay at and when he imparted this information to Angus the latter commented dejectedly: "Honest, Cameron, ye should see this wee Joy. She's a braw bit o' stuff. Dae ye think she'll ivver speak tae me again after this?"

"Of course she wull. You leave aal the explainin' tae me son. I got maself oot o' worst hanks than this afore."

A further visit to the purser's office was necessary so that Cameron and Angus could upgrade their tickets for the longer journey. Whilst there they discovered that it was possible to book overnight cabins on board the *Clansman*. The timetable showed that the vessel was due to leave South Uist at 10 am on

Sunday, calling again at Castlebay for a short time before making the crossing to Oban, arriving at 5 pm.

Installed once more in the lounge bar Cameron tried to console the lovelorn cook.

"Ah'll bet ye any money there'll be a good goin' ceilidh somewherr in 'Boisdale. It'll be jeest furst class," he said.

"Ach, ah`m naw in the mood for ceilidhs an' aal that," came the succinct reply. "Anyhow, hoot's Wullie gaan tae say when he finds oot aboot this?"

"Wullie'll naw know anythin' whativver. Sure we'll be back in Oban for five o'clock the morra' night."

"Aye, well ah jeest hope we urr," answered Angus almost prophetically.

Unknown to the ship's passengers, cocooned in the snugness of the lounge, the vagarious nature of the Scottish weather was in the process of being demonstrated fully. The north-easterly breeze had veered alarmingly and increased steadily in force from the west-south-west, accompanied by rain squalls. By the time the pitching Clansman arrived at Castlebay the wind had reached gale force and only the partial lee of the Hebridean chain enabled her to dock later at Lochboisdale.

Even Cameron had to admit that a run ashore in the conditions prevailing would be folly and after watching television for a while, he and Angus turned in. The wind screamed incessantly through the night and Sunday dawned with no improvement. Meteorology Office forecasts issued at regular intervals warned of storm force ten gales from the Irish Sea to the Butt of Lewis.

"Och, och, we'll jeest have tae sit it oot an' hope it eases soon," said Cameron as Sunday's sailing time passed with no hope of letting go the mooring ropes.

All day long the wind shrieked, driving occasional rain showers horizontally and by late afternoon the stormbound mariners, suffering from the combined effects of too much alcohol and boredom resigned themselves to another night aboard the ferry.

Meanwhile, back on the mainland, Wullie had received the good news that the replacement pump had been picked up by a fish lorry and was due in Oban at 6 pm. He contacted Sandy and arranged for a friend to drive them back to the boat, hoping that Cameron would have the hydraulic system functioning again in a few hours.

Wullie was more than a little surprised to find on their arrival at Oban that the vessel had been subjected to maximum security arrangements and access to her interior was barred by a series of padlocks and chains.

"Och, ah expect that perr o' rascals is aweh fur beer but there wis nae need tae lock her up laik Fort Knox," said an exasperated Wullie, who had no keys of his own. "Come on an' we'll see if we can find them anywherr."

"Any money they're in the Claredon," offered Sandy.

"Aye, right enough," answered Wullie, "ah winna laik tae bet too much that they're naw in there."

The skipper and mate were further mystified by the intelligence bulletin received in the Claredon regarding the whereabouts of their crewmates.

"Hoot the duvvle wid they waant tae go tae Mull for, ah wunner?" mused Wullie, as he and Sandy ordered pints of beer.

The two men were puzzling over the Mull connection in the busy bar, which was being patronised by a good number of fishermen sheltering from the gale, when by one of those fortuitous quirks of fate, Wullie was approached by a chap of similar age. Seconds later it was established that they had been classmates in Glasgow Nautical College many years before when studying for their skipper's certificates.

In a repeat performance of the Cameron - Jeck Sinclair fiasco, one William Andrew Maclean found himself, along with his mate, in a state of jubilation induced by an awesome consumption of Scotland's national drink.

And, while Cameron's boarding of the *Dawn Hunter* had been obstructed by the big ebb tide, Wullie and Sandy faced no such hurdle but they would be unable to penetrate the tightly secured boat.

"We'll jeest haive tae book in here fur the night, Sandy. Aweh an' tell the manager he's got another two beds filled."

Sandy returned minutes later with an apologetic manager who announced with barely disguised relief that the hotel was fully booked and he could not help. When it was established that there was little likelihood of the two drunken mariners finding accommodation at that late hour the manager jokingly invited them to spend the night in an empty horsebox in the back yard, an offer accepted with surprising alacrity.

Sandy's cigarettes and lighter were confiscated and the two men were led to the straw-filled horsebox, to the great amusement of the few customers left in the bar.

"Nae room at the inn," mumbled Wullie as he struggled into a sleeping bag thoughtfully provided by the manager. They bade each other goodnight and were fast asleep within minutes.

Meanwhile across the Minch the wind had abated to some degree and the ferry master announced a possible 3 am departure should there be a further reduction in the severity of the conditions. This turned out to be the case and it was with relief that Cameron and Angus watched the cast off operations at the appointed hour.

They calculated that, taking the scheduled stop at Castlebay into account, the *Clansman* would reach Oban at 09.30.

"Ah wunner if Wullie'll bother tae come back up tae Oban that early on a Mondeh moarnin' Angus," said Cameron.

"Sure ye know he wull. An' we'll be in the soup for naw bein there," came the sound reply.

Almost fully recovered from the excessive alcoholic intake, Cameron and Angus enjoyed a big breakfast on the ferry, which made good time due to the vastly improved conditions. They were, however, worried that Wullie would, indeed, be in Oban and react with asperity at their non-appearance.

The *Clansman* was nearing Oban Bay when Wullie and Sandy awoke in strange surroundings. Shafts of light filtered into the horse-box and Wullie let his eyes become accustomed to the gloom before asking Sandy: "Am ah dreamin' or is this straw we're lyin' on here? Wherr in the wide world urr we?"

"Well, ye're naw dreamin' for a start. As tae wherr we urr, don't ask me."

Struggling out of the sleeping bags they flung open the horsebox door. It took some time for Wullie's faculties to establish their whereabouts and the events of the previous night began to materialise in his fuddled mind.

When they had handed back the sleeping bags and asked the manager for complete confidentiality on the matter, the two dishevelled shipmates made tracks for the Railway Pier.

"Mind, Sandy, if the other two's here, not waan word aboot this."

"Dae ye think ah'm off ma heid?"

The *Dawn Hunter*'s full complement met up again shortly afterwards for the first time in days.

"Heard youse were ower on Mull, Cameron," said the skipper. "This is us jeest arrived an' I'm gled tae see ye locked the boat up weel. How did it go?"

"Och, it wis quite good but we came back across yisterday in case ye wid be here. We steyed last night wae a pal o' mine in Soroba seein' youse wurrna tae be seen," said Cameron. As he moved closer to Wullie, he noted the latter's uneasiness and became aware of a peculiar smell.

Cameron flicked several wisps of straw from his skipper's head and shoulders and inquired:"By the way, it wisna a cattle float youse came up fae Cam'eltoon on by any chance, wis it? Noo, wherr's that pump?"

BLACK FISH

The *Dawn Hunter*'s crew, in common with every other fisherman in Scotland, had cause to be increasingly disgruntled with the government. Fishing policies and restrictions decided upon in Whitehall and Brussels were slowly tightening the noose around an already beleaguered industry.

Many of the new regulations appeared to them to be no more than an appeasement directed towards the U.K.'s European partners and Wullie suspected that deals of another nature were being completed at the expense and to the detriment of fishing. Also, some of the EEC rules were hard to understand. For instance, fish that failed to reach an upset price at auction had to be sprayed with dye and destroyed. It was inadmissible to give it away free to hospitals, schools or the needy, a matter that troubled Wullie's conscience.

Indeed, some of the proposals finding their way across the Channel were actually amusing to the point of being ridiculous. The latest to come to the attention of Wullie and the lads was a quite serious suggestion from Brussels that fishermen should wear hairnets when working on the catch, be it fish, prawns or scallops. Cameron's reaction was typical: "Ah wad need tae get a Norah Batty face mask an a perr o' ootsize wumman's tights tae go alang wae it."

TAC (total allowable catch) figures arrived at by fisheries scientists in recent years had proved to be completely unacceptable to trawlermen with the subsequent quotas being long exhausted before the year's end. This had turned normally honest fishermen into law-breakers.

"There's nae point in throwin' fush that's already deid back intae the watter," was Wullie's philosophical outlook on the subject.

Over quota fish became known as *black fish* and the surreptitious dealings in the various species between fishermen and buyers resulted in greatly increased activity on the part of fishery officers, civil servants employed by the Department of Agriculture and Fisheries for Scotland to police the industry.

The officers, not to be outdone, were quick to adapt to the changing patterns of the fishermen's landing routines and several unfortunate skippers attempting to offload black fish in the wee small hours were caught red-handed. The consequences of such misdemeanours meant court appearances and heavy fines, the severity of which sent shock waves through fishing communities. Some of the tales relating to over-zealous fishery officers had become folklore within the industry. One particularly keen individual was seen to spring from the confines of an empty forty-gallon oil drum to confront a crew landing black fish at four o' clock one morning. And on another occasion a fishery officer was *kidnapped* and taken to sea when he boarded a vessel landing illegal haddock. He was taken back to port only after the crew had dumped the evidence over the side.

Wullie maintained that the authorities should concentrate on law-breaking foreign vessels noted for trawling with illegal nets and retaining immature fish, and leave inshore men to fish in peace.

And so it was, on a late October afternoon, that Wullie noted a sizeable trace of fish on his colour echo sounder. He was ostensibly trawling for prawns in the southern approaches to the Firth of Clyde, but the little pink crustaceans were loath to leave their burrows in the seabed mud, resulting in a depressingly poor day's fishing.

However, Wullie's intrinsic hunting skill took over when he saw the fish mark develop on the sounder and his mood quickly changed from one of almost nonchalance to that of eagerness, rugged determination and keen anticipation. He jumped down from his comfortable helmsman's chair and looked aft over the *Dawn Hunter*'s transom to make sure that the trawl warps leading to the net were in line dead astern, thus ensuring that the gear would come into contact with the shoal.

Wullie decided to trawl for a further 20 minutes, ample time for the fish to become trapped in the cavernous jaws of the net. They would tire after a short time and fall back further towards the cod end, where the catch would accumulate.

This was when Wullie lost his normal aesthetic appreciation of his boat. He saw her now as a deadly predator moving in for the kill that would fill an empty belly and satisfy an enormous appetite.

During the final stages of towing, Wullie had time to reflect on the situation. Most of the Clyde area's fish allocation had been used up. Indeed, with the exception of whiting and hake, the quotas had been exhausted. He tried to convince himself that the boat had hit a big mark of whiting but he knew the species to be too thin on the ground for that. As for hake, they were so scarce that it was now a rare event to net more than a few boxes of even the smallest variety.

Hauling duly commenced and ten minutes later the *Dawn Hunter*'s crew witnessed the spectacle that all fishermen love to see - a net full of big, writhing, thrashing fish. Wullie's fears were fully justified when the net was finally emptied because the catch consisted of 140 boxes of huge prime cod and large coley - or *jacks* as they are known - both species being eagerly sought by buyers, albeit illegally.

The *Dawn Hunter* had hit was generally referred to within the industry as a *droll spot* of cod and coley, an infrequent occurrence, especially in late autumn, but nevertheless not entirely unknown.

"Hoot the duvvle are we gaan tae dae wae this loat boys?" he asked the crew.

Sandy, sensing something of a bonanza wage, retorted as quickly as he could say the words: "Well, we're naw gaan tae dump them, that's fur sure."

"Ah wisna intendin' tae dump them. Ah wis wonderin 'wherr in the name o' fortune we could go wae them," answered Wullie.

Cameron interjected: "Ah don't give wan iota wherr ye go wae them but we better start guttin' them quick. That lot must be worth aboot seeven thousan' poun'. We'll worry aboot dischergin' them when they're ready tae go ashore."

"Aye, yer right Cameron. We'll get underwey an' ah'll try an' get somethin' organised on the 'phone," announced Wullie.

He set a northerly course, though at this point his destination was anything but decided. Wullie was still on a *high*; it was always the same after he had made a particularly successful haul.

He was worried that a wandering fishery protection vessel might intercept him but this was alleviated considerably by the fact that darkness was falling quickly and the inevitable wheeling, diving hordes of seagulls would not be seen surrounding the boat.

Campbeltown was out of the question for landing the illegal fish and Wullie looked longingly to his port hand at the twinkling esplanade lights of the town as the *Dawn Hunter* passed Davaar Island on her northerly flight up Kilbrannan Sound. The boat was almost abeam of Carradale when, after much frenetic telephoning back and forth, it was agreed that Wullie would make for a remote pier on the shores of Loch Riddon, an offshoot of the Kyles of Bute. An articulated lorry, despatched from Glasgow, would rendezvous with the vessel there.

As a young lad on his first boat Wullie remembered sheltering at the little pier for two days during a north-westerly gale and he had never forgotten how quiet the place was, with not even a house to be seen. An ideal location, indeed, to carry out his unlawful act, though it was with a strange sense of foreboding that he steered for Ardlamont Point, at the mouth of the Kyles.

His crewmen, by working in close harmony were at their efficient best and the big catch had been gutted, washed and boxed by the time the *Dawn Hunter* reached the mouth of Loch Riddon. Despite the fact that there were no visible signs of habitation, Wullie switched off the boat's navigation lights and slowed his speed to a crawl. Twenty minutes later the *Dawn Hunter* was alongside the stone jetty, which had been pinpointed with unerring accuracy by her five-foot radar scanner.

"Wherr the hell's that larry?" he agonised. "If ah get caught wae this lot on board it's the Bar L jyle ah'll end up in. Take the big torch oot o' the ingine-room an' see if ye can see anythin' up the rodd a wee bit Angus, that's the boy."

Angus dutifully walked the half mile along the single track byway until he came to its junction with the Strachur - Tighnabruaich road, where an articulated lorry bearing the name *Edwards - THE Fish Merchants* was parked in a thoroughly precarious manner.

The cook hurriedly introduced himself to the driver, who was showing signs of annoyance.

"Whit the dickens dae ye think ye're playin' at? Ah'll never get this motor doon that wee road in a month o' Sundays, never mind back up wae a load o' fish on."

"Ye better come quick an' tell the skipper then because ivvery tail aboard the boat is on a black fush, " Angus replied.

After a quick consultation with Wullie the Glasgow driver announced there was only one thing for it and that was to send for another smaller lorry to transfer the fish in stages from the boat to the larger vehicle.

Things were complicated further when Wullie's cellular telephone reception was found to be poor due to the boat's position and he had to walk to the lorry and be driven to the nearest telephone kiosk some three miles away in order to make the necessary arrangements with the fish buyer.

"Och, how wis ah naw putt on this earth tae be a joiner, or a mechanic, or a plumber. Anythin' but a fusherman," lamented the skipper who by this time was pacing up and down the jetty in a state of extreme agitation whilst awaiting the arrival of the second truck.

The eventual appearance of a much smaller vehicle, which had hired by the Glasgow buyer from an Arrochar agricultural contractor, calmed Wullie marginally and minutes later the first of the illegal consignment was being swung ashore. It was soon estimated that three trips would have to be made by the Arrochar man before the *Dawn Hunter* would be rid of her illegal cargo.

The articulated lorry, with twin amber hazard lights in operation, was parked partially blocking the main road just clear of its junction with the single track. Skilful manoeuvring brought the smaller wagon containing the fish and the *Dawn Hunter*'s crew' *back to back* with the fourteen wheeler and the six men soon had the boxes transferred.

However, the clockwork operations of the second transhipment were abruptly halted when a Strathclyde Police patrol car arrived on the scene. The blood in Wullie's veins ran cold and his stomach descended to somewhere in the region of his seaboots as he turned a whiter shade of pale.

The single occupant of the police car, a young constable in his mid-twenties approached the lorries with a puzzled look on his face. "Would you mind telling me just exactly what is going on here please," he implored his audience.

Catching on immediately to the policeman's unmistakable Kelvinside accent, Wullie clutched an exceedingly thin straw.

"Well, constable, we wur steamin' through the Kyles o' Bute makin' for Tarbert tae land oor catch and did the blinkin' ingine naw go an' overheat on us. We had tae come intae the wee quay doon on the shore o' Loch Riddon there tae let it cool off and we thocht it wid be as well if we jeest landed the fush while we wur here. The big larry canna make it doon tae the boat so we have tae take the fush up a wee drap at a time on the other motor here."

"Ye're naw a man fae these parts, I can tell that aalright. Wherr aboots urr ye stationed an' dae ye laik it roon' aboot here?"

"Oh, yes. My wife is a schoolteacher and she fancied a quiet little country school. I was quite taken with the idea of a wee office myself so I applied for a transfer from the city force. I now hold fort in a country station up in Glendaruel," replied the bobby in all innocence.

The Maclean guile was in overdrive.

"Man, ah'll bet ye any money that ye jeest love fush, you bein' a Glesca man. Luft yer car boot a meenut an' the boys'll sling in a box o' braw cod for yer freezer in case ye get cut off up that glen in the deid o' wunter."

"Heavens, that's really generous of you skipper. Thank you very, very much."

"Think naethin' merr o' it," said Wullie now fully convinced that he had this particular branch of the long arm of the law well and truly in the palm of his hand.

"I'd better put down a couple of warning signs and cones. There's a big NFU meeting in Tighnabruaich tonight and, as it is getting late, it is bound to be dispersing soon."

Sure enough, a little later there was a trickle of traffic past the scene of the crime. The constable was fully engaged in directing cars when Cameron, in an aside to Wullie, hissed: "How in the name o' God did you manage this?"

"Och, it wis easy. Ah tweeged right aweh that he wis a city boy and when he said he wis stationed up in Glendaruel it wis obvious he wouldna be very well versed in the weys o' fushin.' The sowel will hardly have a clue aboot quotas an' things laik that. Them Glesca boys can be very Heilan' at times ye know.

"Mind you, I winna haive dreamt o' tryin' it on wae the polis in Tarbert, or Carradale, or Cam'eltoon. Naw, naw, that wid be really askin' for it, them bein' so weel acquent aboot things that really metter."

The loading of the fish was soon completed, under the supervision of the well-intentioned but rather naive policeman. Making sure that the load was safely tied down, he waved the articulated lorry on it's way before collecting the various road safety items he had meticulously placed around the scene.

Bidding Wullie and the crew farewell, the constable once again thanked them for the gift of the cod and said: "Well, it has been a most interesting night for me. I'll be thinking about you boys when I sit down to my first meal of cod and chips." Under his breath, one William Andrew Maclean muttered: "An' ah'll be havin' nightmares aboot you fur the next month."

DEVOTEES OF MARCONI

"Dae ye know somethin,' Angus. Ah canna understaan' how fushermen got on afore there wis wirelesses in boats," stated the skipper.

Wullie and Angus were on watch in the *Dawn Hunter's* wheelhouse as she steamed her purposeful way towards the Sound of Jura prawn grounds in the early hours of a tranquil July morning. The companionable silence on the bridge was frequently punctuated by crackling radio talk of all kinds on the boat's two sets, ranging from seriously philosophical skippers' conversations to light-hearted banter among the more youthful watchkeepers.

"Aye, right enough," answered Angus. "Ah suppose it's a braw thing tae have on a boat. He wis a right brenny man, that Marconi, an' that's a fact."

"Man you're right there, Angus, he was cluvver tae make such a wonderful invention.

"Mind you, it wisna jeest so bad in the real owld days when aal the skiffs were at the ring-nettin' along the shore for herrin.' They wur that close tae wan another they could shout across but this traalin' stuff on the open sea nooadehs is a different baall gemme entirely."

The conversation was interrupted by a beckoning call on the gleaming Sailor 144 VHF radio.

"*Dawn Hunter, Dawn Hunter. Harvest Dawn*, are ye receivin' me Wullie, over."

"*Harvest Dawn*, aye, ah'm gettin' ye fine Coalin. Hoot's the crack this moarnin,' over."

"Shift her up tae that other channel an ah'll get a yarn wae ye."

Angus settled himself more comfortably in the narrow second watchkeeper's cushioned bench alongside the big helmsman's chair that Wullie occupied. He knew from experience that a change of channel from the normal intership frequency meant the two skippers were about to display their full appreciation of Marconi and would be fully occupied on the radio for some time.

He knew, also, that the chat on channel 71 would inevitably veer from the more serious aspects of the job to matters of much less gravity and, subsequently, be more entertaining.

Angus was right, for Colin McMurchy on the *Harvest Dawn*, after giving Wullie a brief resume of his fishing intentions and receiving similar information in return, shifted tack and let a more jocular strain filter into the conversation.

One of the advantages of having VHF radio installed was that it afforded skippers direct contact with shore-based fishselling agents when it came to relaying messages concerning the various pieces of chandlery, provisions or fuel required at landing time. The boats usually took turns at passing on the collective requests on one call. Colin told Wullie of an incident, which occurred the previous week that made Angus snigger.

A very naive young man had just been appointed office assistant in one of the fishselling firms. The fact that he was a green youngster quite oblivious of the fact that some skippers were blessed with a very sardonic nature, coupled with his eager desire to please, made him extremely vulnerable to attack. The fleet was fishing on the Gigha prawn grounds and one skipper, highly dissatisfied with his catches, reckoned that his trawl had come to the end of a useful life and would have to be replaced.

"Aye, I'm afraid it's the paraffin oil for it," he said making reference to a hypothetical expression widely used by skippers suggesting destruction by fire, though completely imaginary, of the discarded net.

Colin described how the skipper entrusted with the relaying of all messages to the office that day made an earnest request for a two gallon can of paraffin to be included in the stores ordered by the *Prosperity*. Sure enough, the paraffin arrived at the Tayinloan jetty, where the vessels were landing. Stuck on the side of the can was a large piece of card on which was written: *For Prosperity's net*. Apparently the young man had asked a senior colleague what purpose the paraffin served on a trawl net and was told that fishing results increased greatly if the oil was rubbed vigorously into the netting.

Two days later the young man was subjected to another hoax request that he dutifully carried out.

Although it was during the second week of July and temperatures were in the 70's, Colin told how the reporting-in skipper that day informed the young salesman that his crew were feeling very cold out on the high seas - despite the fact that they were close enough to land to see vehicles moving around on the Kintyre Peninsula - and that the cook wished to make a massive pot of Scotch broth to take the chill out of their bones.

He asked that a sheep's head be sent to Tayinloan along with the rest of the vessel's stores so that the soup could be made in the old-fashioned Scottish way. It had, of course, been many years since he had heard of anyone using the ancient Scots recipe and he reckoned the salesman would be highly embarrassed by the reaction to his request at the butcher's shop.

The joke backfired, however, due to the boat orders that day being processed by the most elderly of the shop staff who did in fact procure a sheep's head from the abbatoir, commenting that the old recipes were the best.

"Aye, Wullie, seemin'ly aal hell wis let loose at Tayinloan when they opened the bag an' saw a sheep's heid lookin' up at them," said Colin.

Chuckling to himself, Angus made a speedy visit to the galley where he brewed two mugs of strong tea and came back to find Wullie talking about engines and the various vessels' steaming speeds.

"Och, ah'll need tae tell ye aboot the time we wur makin' for the heid o' West Loch Tarbert tae land, Colin. We passed a wee forty-fitt boat caalled the *Incentive* on the way. Ah think she had a hunner an' ten horse power Gardner in her but the owld skipper thought she could go laik the duvvle.

"She wis shallow-draughted an' hadna got a right grup o' the watter at aal. In fact ah don't believe she could puhll the tell off a sweetie moose.

"Anyway, he caalled me up on channel eight an' asked me hoot kind o' ingine we had. I telt him it wis a three hunner Cat and he replied at wance wae the words: 'Well I think some o' yer pussies are deid because I believe we're catchin' you'."

"Aye, Wullie, the patter can be good on the wireless when ivveryboody's in good trum," continued Colin as Wullie sipped his tea.

"Aal the same, some o' them make a right eediot o' themselves when they come on. Laik the fella fae Dunure that announced wan deh that Madonna wis a sex syllable. That wis him that thocht ye caalled a bin wagon a refugee lorry. Ah think it wis the same man that said a bloke came tae his dorr an' asked him tae sign a partition tryin' tae stop a new pub gettin' beelt. Did ye get that, over?"

"Got you all ok, Colin. Aye, an' hoot aboot the man that said he had a cartoon o' ice cream the other day? Or the fella that caalled thon cowld French northerly wund the minstrel. Then there wis the poor sowell that thought an ombudsman drove wan o' the West Coast Motors buses."

Angus was by this time thoroughly enjoying the radio narrative and was all ears when Colin commented on some of the lies he had heard transmitted over the years.

"Jings, it's laik the liar o' the year contest wae some o' them, Wullie, isn't it? It jeest comes as saicond nature tae them skippers tae either let on they're naw receivin' ye or else it's a pack o' damn't fibs ye get."

Wullie and Colin were, generally speaking, honest with each other on the air when discussing fishing but a number of other skippers apparently found it impossible to tell the truth when using the radio.

Referring to one infamous individual, Colin asked Wullie: "Can ye naw mind the time Cherlie 'Tyre dinna let on aboot the sixty boxes o' cod he had an' aal the buyers were aweh hame by the time he got in? That yin cost him dear because he wis forced tae consign his fush tae the Glesca market at rockbottom prices. An' he had tae pay for the larry as well."

Wullie replied: "Aye, but hoot aboot the wans that tell lies the other way? Ah mind we wur fushin' up Kilbrannan Soon' wae a few other boats an' wan fella kept reportin' nearly double the amount we wis catchin. Ah'm tellin' ye, ah wis nearly off ma heid wunnerin' how tae alter oor gear so that we could get the same as him. We tried ivverythin' we could think o' but I could have brennned him when I saw hoot he landed on tae the fush market. It wis aboot haalf o' whit we had oorselfs."

"Aye, they're naw easy some o' them, right enough."

At this juncture a loud voice bellowed from the speaker and reverberated around the wheelhouse: "Come on, Wullie, gie us wan o' yer favourite country an' western sangs."

The booming interjection came from Ian Jamieson, skipper of the scallop dredger *Quest* and a devoted fan of the American- style music. Though blessed with possibly the strongest vocal chords in the fleet, Ian had great difficulty in organising them into any semblance of harmony and, thankfully, left the singing to others.

Wullie, no mean crooner himself, usually carried his accoustic guitar aboard the boat and he withdrew it from its special locker before launching into an animated and illegal performance of *Don't take your love to town* as Angus held the transmitter's handset trigger in the open position.

"Man, that wis braw aalthegither, Wullie," a grateful Ian radioed at the completion of the song, though Skipper Maclean's youthful assistant wished he had been aiding in the performance of a number by Oasis or Boyzone.

Wullie had recently undergone an examination in advanced radiotelephony procedure at Glasgow as part of the upgrading of his fishing vessel master's certificate. He had enjoyed the camaraderie with other mariners in the city's nautical college so much that he extended the short course by a few days to include expert tuition in signalling, using the morse code by Aldis lamp method. As was usual when Wullie committed himself to an undertaking, he emerged from the test with commendable results, much to his inner delight.

Angus refilled the big mugs with strong tea yet again just as the *Dawn Hunter* rounded the Mull of Kintyre. Steaming south east at a considerable rate of knots from the direction of the Sound of Islay to meet them was one of Her Majesty's warships.

It was one of the Royal Navy's newest frigates and it presented a wonderful picture in the watery sunlight of a day newly dawned. A huge wave creamed from either side of her majestic flared bow as massive engines drove her sleek grey hull relentlessly onward. The boiling maelstrom at her stern created by two huge thrashing propellers rose to deck level before gradually flattening out to leave a wake astern as far as the eye could see.

Wullie and Angus were enthralled by the spectacle and the cook unearthed his camera to record the moment for posterity. "Maybe the local paper'll use this nixt week," said the keen amateur photographer but his skipper was only half listening.

As the frigate drew closer, Wullie manipulated the powerful wheelhouse roof-mounted Francis 14-inch searchlight until it was trained on the navyman. Utilising his recently acquired skills in signalling Wullie proficiently sent the message: 'You are beautiful'.

Without hesitation the warship's big Aldis lamp flashed into life and conveyed the witty thoughts of the duty signaller across the shimmering water with the reply: 'I bet you say that to all the ships'!

"Hoot are ye laughin' at noo?" enquired Angus.

"Well, son, ah suppose ah could seh a wumman has jeest rejected me," was Wullie's enigmatic reply.

GLEKKIT YINS

Though Angus was basically a bright enough young lad he occasionally let his teenage mind wander to other more important matters such as girls, rock music and football whilst carrying out his duties as a fisherman, resulting in minor chaos aboard the *Dawn Hunter*.

The three deckies were hard at work sifting through a big haul of prawns one Friday afternoon in Kilbrannan Sound and were anxious to clear the deck before the last tow of the week was completed. Wullie tended to make Friday's last haul a short one so that the crew would have time to attend to the catch and give the boat a thorough scrub down at the harbour while he attended to the settling up of the wages.

The larger prawns, more suited to the French and Spanish markets, are kept alive but the tails only of the smaller ones are retained for the UK scampi processors. Wullie was, as usual, periodically observing deck activities from his lofty position in the wheelhouse. Unfortunately for Angus, who for the previous few minutes had been mentally practising how to secure the affections of a girl called Annette MacKenzie - a long time target - the skipper's gaze fell upon him as he absent-mindedly threw a handful of prawn tails over the side and the equivalent number of heads and offal into his basket.

"In the name o' the wee man, wid ye stop being so glekkit, Angus," roared the angry Wullie.

Ears burning, Angus inquired of Cameron: "Hoot does glekkit mean anyweh?" Cameron did not have the heart to tell Angus that the word, derived from the Gaelic *gleogach* and spelt *glaikit* in Scots dictionaries, meant among other things: Thoughtless, dazed, silly, foolish, giddy, volatile.

Instead, he tried to lessen Angus's embarrassment by saying: "Ach, it jeest means ye maybe werena peyin' right attention, that's aal."

"Naw, ah don't think so," continued the cook. "Ye're jeest tryin' tae pan me off wae any owld explanation. Come on, tell me hoot glekkit means."

"Well, ah'll tell ye a wee story aboot a fella that wis glekkit, son, an' ye can work it oot for yersel' if ye faal intae the same category."

Cameron proceeded to tell Angus about a deckhand aboard a vessel called the *Western Isles* who was never happy with traditional Scottish fare and who put constant pressure on the cook to come up with meals of a more exotic nature, advocating the use of obscure herbs and spices.

Tired of the constant griping, the boat's cook informed the deckie that he would, as a special favour, prepare him a curry. The latter was delighted when, that evening, as the rest of the crew sat down to a hearty feast of haddock and chips, a plateful of curry and boiled rice was put down in front of him.

Enthusing over his Asian repast, the deckie informed his shipmates that they did not realise what they were missing and he praised the cook's efforts highly saying that the curry tasted exactly as it should.

The rest of the crew, though, had difficulty in concealing their amusement as they watched the man work his way through his curry, the main ingredient of which was a tin of prime dog meat.

"The cook used the doag meat tae try an' putt him off the notion o' fancy foreign grub," said Cameron.

"But he dinna tweeg an' he still thinks tae this day that he wis eatin' curried beef. Noo, that's whit ah wad caall glekkit."

"Aye," remarked Sandy who had been listening with interest, "ah suppose that wis glekkit right enough but ah can tell ye wan that takes some batin'."

Wullie by this time had shown an interest in the yarn, though he was pleased to note that the deckies still worked feverishly as they talked among themselves.

Sandy continued: "It was the year ah wis on the wee *Silver Spray* alang wae Kenny Black. We wis daein' fine, jeest the two o' us, at the lobsters an' the velvet crabs."

"Anyweh, durin' the Glesca Ferr, a fella asked if he could come oot wae us for the deh an' we said it wid be aalright. The deh he came started off fine aalthegither but as the moarnin' wore on a fresh breeze came aweh an' the wee boat began bouncin' aboot a bit.

"It wisna lang afore the bloke started tae look a bit green an' a wee while efter that he wis spewin' his hert oot. Durin' wan o' the bouts his faalse teeth flew oot an' shot clean ower the side intae the watter."

Sandy went on to tell how, on hauling the next fleet of creels, his mate Kenny, as a joke, took out his own top set of teeth and slipped them into one of the lobster pots before triumphantly exclaiming that the lost dentures had been recovered.

Before either of the two fishermen could make a move, the Glasgow man had the teeth in his mouth. He decided, however, that they did not fit and could therefore not be his, so he promptly threw them back into the sea - to Kenny's utter disbelief.

"Noo, if that wisna being glekkit, ah don't know hoot wis," concluded Sandy.

"Aye, but who wis the glekkit yin, Kenny or the Glesca man?" asked Wullie through an open wheelhouse window. Mind you, ah wance sailed wae a fella fae Arran that wis pretty glekkit."

The unfortunate islander, Wullie explained, was apparently sadly lacking in the grey matter department, though physically a tireless and conscientious fisherman.

"Ah mind ah asked him wance if the kettle wis boilin' an' did he naw go an' stick his haan' intae it tae find oot. Another time we wis lyin' at anchor at Pladda an' a wild thick fog came doon on us durin' the night. The Arranman wis first up in the moarnin' an' when he went oot on dake he shouted doon tae us: 'Come up here tae ye see this boys, ye can see naethin'.'"

Wullie recalled the occasion when the Arran chap was sent ashore for provisions at Tobermory, a mission which included a visit to the local butcher's shop where he encountered no problems at all until he made a request for a quantity of beef link sausages.

"The butcher asked him how many sassidges he wis waantin' an' instead o' sehin' a couple o' punn, or three punn, the Arranman scratched his heid. Then he stuck oot his two erms an' said: 'Och, jeest gie me a fathom o' links please'.

When the laughter had subsided, Cameron contributed what he reckoned was another "wee gem" concerning gleogairs.

The occasion, he said, had started off as a sombre affair - the scattering of his great-uncle's ashes on Campbeltown Loch.

"The owld sowell steyed in Edinburgh for a long time an' he wis cremated there. But he made sure afore he went that ivveryboady knew that he waanted his ashes spread on his beloved loch."

When the sad day arrived Cameron arranged for the family and close friends to gather together aboard one of the local boats to witness the carrying out of his great-uncle Jamie's last request, the short service being conducted by the local Wee Free minister.

"Ivverythin' wis gaan jeest fine an' the boat stopped in the muddle o' the loch. The munister had told owld Jamie's son he wid gie him a wink when the right time came for him tae empty the casket ower the side, which wis ferr enough.

"Hoot they dinna realise though wis that while the munister wis sehin' the prayer the boat had fell roon across the wee breeze that wis blowin' and when he signalled mah cousin tae dae the necessary he wis that glekkit he never thought aboot the wund or anythin' else.

"When he shook oot the ashes the whole issue blew back aboard the boat. It wis aal ower mah black suit an' stuck in mah herr gel; ivveryboady got it. Ah even saw the munister spittin' poor owld Uncle Jamie back oot in disgust an' he wisna lang in terminatin' the service ah can tell ye.

"Aye, ye wid need a damned good refreshment efter that mush," chuckled Wullie. He went on: "Sandy, you'll have mind o' thon droll eediot that wis aboard wae us for a wee while, have ye naw?"

When the mate nodded his agreement Wullie proceeded to enlighten Cameron and Angus on the dubious attributes of one Daniel McGerrity, a Glasgow man who had joined the *Dawn Hunter* on a trial basis for a month and who had been asked to leave after a week.

"He wis aye complainin' wae the toothache. An' nae wunner for ah nivver saw a mooth laik that in aal my life afore. Ah' m tellin' ye, he had a set o' teeth laik a row o' condemned hooses .

"Ah went oot intae the galley wan deh an' there he wis squeezin a whole tube o' toothpaste intae his jaaws tae he wis foamin' at the mooth. Ah asked him hoot he wis daein' an' he pointed tae the empty tube wherr it said: 'Fights tooth decay'.

" Ah jeest shook mah heid an' telt him it wis a wee bit late for that but he genuinely thought he wid get better.

"Och, Angus, ah nearly forgot tae tell ye aboot Glekkit Neilly," continued Wullie who by this time was really warming to the yarn.

"He's as thick as his name suggests. Ah'm tellin ye, there's merr brenns in a rockin' horse."

It appeared that one Neil Sutherland, better known in the area as Glekitt Neilly had won himself a job on a construction site in Kintyre that was preparing a vast area in readiness for the fabrication of oil platforms.

Sutherland was quick to latch on to the fact that the huge workforce was largely unsupervised and he took full advantage of this. After a week or so of shirking his duties around the site he took to spending most of the day in the village pub three miles distant.

Unfortunately, the more Sutherland drank the louder his voice became. Conversely his sense of reasoning and tact dipped alarmingly so that it came as no real surprise when, after consuming eight pints of heavy one day, he suddenly found himself reduced to the unenviable state of unemployment once more.

Sutherland, apparently, was spouting forth to the assembled company about how easy It was to pick up his £400 wages each week for doing hardly any work at all.

"Ah jeest turn up an' clock in ivvery moarnin' an' waander aboot the place till openin' time. Then I get wan o' the larry drivers tae gie me a run doon here. I wis nivver so well aff in mah life. Look at my hands, they're naw even the slightest wee bit durty - that jeest shows youse how little work I have done the deh."

At this juncture as authoritative voice drifted across the bar: "And you'll be doing a damned sight less as from this instant." It was the site agent, a man previously unknown to Sutherland.

Wullie concluded: "Aye, it's a good job we've got aal wur wuts an' faculties aboot us - well some o' us at any rate," his eyes resting on the junior crew member. It was time for Angus to come to his own defence.

"Surely youse don't think ah'm as droll an' light in the heid as them eediots youse have been speakin' aboot, or dae ye?"

The crew had to admit that, on reflection, their long-suffering cook could not be bracketed along with some of the more glekkit characters in the area and, as a special treat, he was told he could buy the first round that night in the Wee Toon Bar.

GENERAL CARGO

It was the time of the year that Wullie loathed. Trawl fishing, almost without exception, usually ground to a very unprofitable halt around the beginning of May, when both fish and prawns seemed to disappear from the tried and trusted patches for a few weeks before returning as before - an obvious quirk of nature. This barren period was usually accompanied by a spell of fine weather and traditionally saw most of the fleet tethered for anything up to three weeks, which enabled the skippers and crews to carry out painting and general refit work.

For Wullie it was a time of financial strain. Although he was extremely proud of his vessel and liked to keep her in pristine condition, it was a costly business when it came to buying paint and other materials required for her annual overhaul, as well as having to pay the crew for doing the work.

In direct contrast, Sandy, Cameron and Angus, for different reasons, enjoyed the lay-off time immensely. For Sandy it meant hours exploring sunken wrecks in his skin-diving suit, ever hopeful of turning up something of real value. Cameron's leisure time was spent in searches of a different kind - the pursuit of the female species on a nightly basis. And for Angus, an accomplished amateur footballer, automatic selection to the leading local team without the threat of not being able to make the kick-off time due to fishing's haphazard hours meant a great deal to him.

It was during the first week of *cleaning time,* just as the boat's hull had been brought back to her shining best, when Angus reported after the lunch break that his mother, who worked as a part-time receptionist in the seafront Royal Hotel, had some information concerning a newly-arrived guest which she felt sure would interest Wullie. She had asked that Wullie call in at the hotel at the end of the day's painting, when she would explain.

As the day wore on Wullie became more and more puzzled as to the identity of the mysterious resident. He finally announced that curiosity had got the better of him and he abandoned work for the day.

"Thank hivvens for that. Ah could murder a pint o' lager shandy," said Cameron as the *Dawn Hunter*'s crew strolled up the Old Quay in the warm sunshine of a lovely May afternoon.

All hands retired to the Royal where Cameron immediately attended to the important matter of refreshment while Wullie had a few words with Angus's mother.

It transpired that a certain Mr. Peterson had arrived in town to secure the use of two fishing boats for the transportation of goods from Scotland to Northern

Ireland on behalf of his company, a major departmental store chain. A nationwide seaman's strike was starting to bite and his firm's shops across the water were beginning to feel the effects, with floor managers reporting shortages of many items.

Angus's mother was immediately alert to the obvious financial gains involved and told Mr. Peterson that she would arrange a meeting with Wullie, a man she described as hard working, honest and reliable.

"Jeest go through tae the bar an' ah'll get him tae come an' see ye Wullie," she said.

Five minutes later a tall, distinguished looking well-dressed man entered the small lounge bar, the only occupants of which were the men of the *Dawn Hunter*.

"Good afternoon gentlemen, my name is Alan Peterson and I represent the head office of Econobuys Limited. Although we do not have a store in Campbeltown at present, I am sure you will have heard of us."

When the crew nodded and murmured their assent Peterson called for the replenishment of everyone's glass before establishing the identity of the skipper.

"Well, Captain Maclean, the position is quite simple. The seamens' strike is having a knock-on effect in our Irish branches and we have to get various lines across to them soon. It appears that our only hope lies in the chartering of a couple of fishing trawlers, on a regular basis, to run the goods to the Emerald Isle."

Wullie positively glowed at Peterson's reference to his status on the *Dawn Hunter*. Never before had he been referred to as *captain* and he took to the man immediately, though he warned himself to be cautious when the inevitable discussion of hiring fees came up.

Peterson continued: "If you are agreeable, and can find me one other vessel for the job we can discuss the financial arrangements over dinner as my guest here in the hotel tonight. Bring your good lady along if you wish."

Wullie accepted the executive's offer and arranged to return to the hostelry later that evening.

"Mind you an' ask for plenty," was Sandy's parting shot to his skipper as the *Dawn Hunter*'s crew dispersed at the hotel's front door.

Wullie had just washed down an exceedingly appetising serving of pate de fois gras with an equally agreeable wine when Peterson broached the subject of money.

"Och well, we'll be missin' a dacent fushin' o' prawns so it will need tae be well worth oor while. Ah reckon we wid need aboot a thousand poun' a run," suggested Wullie.

"Good grief William," countered Peterson, "we weren't exactly looking to the charter of a container ship. And furthermore, I have done my homework and I know that the fishing in these parts is virtually non-existent at the moment." A further few minutes haggling resulted in the figure of £700 per run being decided upon.

"There are obviously some perks with the job," Peterson continued. "We always make allowances for loss through breakages and provided your crew don't participate in an orgy of wholesale piracy we would turn a blind eye if you helped yourself to a few items."

Wullie's wife, Anne, laughed inwardly as she listened to Peterson and thought of Sandy, who, she reckoned would surely think it was Christmas time.

Painting work was abandoned aboard the *Dawn Hunter* the following morning when Wullie announced the news. Fish room stanchions and boards were replaced by the lads and the hold was made ready to receive cargoes, the composition of which were light years from the mind of the naval architect who had designed the boat.

Wullie's pal James MacLeod, better known as Jamie Gloud, owned a boat of similar dimensions named the *Bounteous* and it was arranged that she would participate in the Irish runs also, much to the delight of her crew.

Both boats, diesels murmuring quietly and with the crews turned out to the man, were ready with discharging derricks raised when an enormous Econobuys articulated lorry arrived in Campbeltown early the next day. It was soon established that the first cargo consisted of a consignment of pre-packed potatoes and long-life milk, a matter that flustered the avaricious Sandy greatly. "This is jeest laik takin' bloody coals tae Newcastle," he grumbled as he realised there would be no worthwhile plunder on the first trip.

"Ah wid cerry coal tae anywherr if the cash wis right. For goodness seck don't forget we're on seeven hunner poun' a trup Sandy, an' therr'll be plenty o' chances tae get a wee bit scran later on," countered the skipper.

The inaugural runs of the *Dawn Hunter* and the *Bounteous*, both vessels loaded to the hatches, passed off without incident. The calculated tidal conditions in the Sound of Sanda turned out to be ideal and the boats completed the journey to Red Bay, Co. Antrim, in four hours, where the goods were loaded onto two smaller stranded Econobuys lorries for distribution to various stores around the Province.

Cameron increased his popularity among several young ladies in the town at the completion of the next trip two days later. In the cargo were several large cardboard cases of women's tights and a quantity of female toiletries, some of which the bold MacPherson purloined. The items in question were presented to selected females who frequented his favourite lounge bar and some of them went home that night with bulging handbags.

Sandy's prayers were answered on the third trip when it was seen that the load consisted entirely of cigarettes.... millions of them. The mate stashed away enough to keep him puffing for months. He was not so lucky, though, on the following voyage, which was made with a mixed cargo that included a substantial number of boxes which contained musical compact discs. Although he certainly could not be termed an avid music lover, Sandy reckoned a box of CD's to add to the house collection would be most welcome.

Each carton contained 100 discs and the musically uneducated mate selected one marked *Assorted* in the mistaken belief he was gaining that number of different titles. He was dumbfounded, however, when he opened the box on returning home to find that it held 100 identical CD's by a heavy rock group known universally as *The Assorted.* Things were made worse when his son, Calum, mentioned the matter to Wullie's boy in the billiard room of the local community centre who, in turn, told the skipper.

Cameron rose to the occasion admirably and the relentless teasing of Sandy, accompanied by Angus's ear piercing renderings of *The Assorted's* work, continued for days.

Two weeks later, the strike still showed no signs of ending and Wullie was approached by a local sawmilling contractor who was most anxious to have a load of wooden fence posts delivered to the Isle of Colonsay. He reckoned the run could be accomplished easily between Econobuys assignments, but he cleared the position with Peterson before hammering out an acceptable price with the woodman.

Though the *Dawn Hunter's* hold was crammed to deck level with the fence stobs, a considerable number still lay on the quayside and the crew had to stow them on deck. Being ignorant of coastal trade procedure, the deck cargo was, to say the least, positioned in a very haphazard fashion and the unfortunate consequences were the loss of a fair number of the posts.

Everything had gone well until the boat nosed out of the Sound of Islay on the last lap of her journey to Scalasaig Pier, on Colonsay. The notoriously unpredictable Scottish West Coast weather, however, lived up to its reputation and suddenly produced an unwelcome strong breeze out of the west-south-west. It was the most awkward direction possible for the *Dawn Hunter's* course and the vessel began to roll heavily. The motion assisted by the water breaking over the boat's beam eventually caused part of the inadequately stowed cargo to shift and be washed overboard. Wullie grimaced with every wave that struck and said: "Ah hope them fermers on Colonsay canna coont very weel."

As it happened, the Colonsay men displayed formidable mathematical dexterity and announced a shortfall of 57 posts when discharging operations terminated.

"Well, ah jeest canna understaan' how there's some missin' boys," Wullie told the small gathering of islanders. "Unless yer man in Cam'eltoon made a mistake when he wis loadin' them on tae his larry."

"Or unless they are maybe being washed ashore at Glengarrisdale Bay on Jura chust at thiss meenute on account off a good breeze off wind that iss blowing," suggested a lilting island voice.

"I'm thinking we'll chust away up and phone over to the sawmill and tell heem to alter the account accordingly, since the paling stabs were paid for in advance."

"Och, there's nae need for that. Ah wis responsible for the cargo an' ah'll staan' good any loss youse have suffered," answered Wullie.

"Hoot kind o' price is a fence post anyweh?" he enquired.

Without hesitation the islander replied: "Exactly one pound sixty pence. Come away up to the hotel for a dram, you and your boys, and we'll haff a yarn about it."

Wullie had for years held that a few *wee whuskies* had the most calming and beneficial effect on man but despite having downed four in the hotel bar that evening his frame of mind was anything but tranquil as he made out a cheque for £91.20.

The *Dawn Hunter*'s crewmen were contemplating their return to the boat when an islander by the name of Robert MacKinnon, a man well known to Wullie, appeared on the scene.

"Man, man, Wullie Clane, and how iss yourself? It must be seffen or eight years since I clapped my eyes on you."

The crew resigned themselves to a delayed departure from Colonsay while the skipper and Robert talked over old times as they refreshed themselves with whisky.

When Wullie discovered that Robert still had a considerable collection of laying ducks he requested a few of the eggs for the boat.

"Ah'm tellin' you Angus mah boy, ye've nivver tasted the laiks o'a juck's egg alang wae yer brekkfast," he informed the cook.

"And how would you like a nice big fat juicy duck for the table ass well?" inquired Robert. Wullie nodded acceptance.

"You would? Well I know how keen you are to get away so I'll chust neep back to the croft and get the cailleach to peeck out a good one for you. I'll not be two shakes off a lamb's tail."

True to his word, Robert returned shortly afterwards with one dozen eggs and the promised fowl. Expecting to be given a plucked bird the crew were nonplussed when the Colonsay man produced a very much alive and quacking duck from an old grain sack.

"Chust shove her down into the boat's hold until you are ready to eat her. You could use wan off the wing pockets ass a kind off hutch and Angus there could fed her with scraps," advised Robert as he waved the *Dawn Hunter* farewell from Colonsay.

The duck was immediately taken down to the depths of the boat and christened Henrietta by Cameron, called for a Campbeltown girl of that name who "waddled aboot jeest the very same as that burd." Sandy boxed in a wing compartment to be used as a temporary home and Henrietta was ceremoniously placed on a comfortable bed of soft nylon netting.

The leftovers from each meal during the next few days were scraped into a special *Henrietta dish* and Angus, as appointed duck welfare officer, descended into the fishroom regularly to feed the feathered guest, whose appetite almost matched that of the crew.

Returning from a trip to Red Bay shortly afterwards Wullie suggested a roast duck dinner for the following day and ordered Angus to "thraw the burd's neck" so that it could be plucked in readiness for the oven. Angus, for the first time in his seagoing career, flatly refused to comply with the command, as did Sandy and Cameron when Wullie approached them.

"It wad jeest be laik committin' a murder. Naw, ah'm naw haivin' that on my conscience, an' neether is Cameron or Angus," Sandy told Wullie with conviction. "Och, youse is jeest a crowd o' big Jessies, honestly. Aweh an' turn in an' ah'll dae it maself. It'll naw be that when youse is sittin' doon tae a braw feed o' roast duck an' aal the trummin's," replied the skipper.

With the crew safely in their bunks, Wullie left the *Dawn Hunter* on autopilot and prepared to carry out the execution. By the time he had regained the deck with Henrietta cradled in his arms, however, the thought of the bird roasting in the boat's galley oven reviled him. He gently dropped her over the side into the Sound of Sanda, and Henrietta made off with impressive rapidity for the shores of Dunaverty Bay, where she would no doubt find a good home on one of the many farms in the area.

The crew greeted Wullie's explanation of Henrietta's disappearance with complete satisfaction.

"Ah nivver saw a burd move quicker in aal my life afore. Ah putt it doon for an instant an' it wis ower the side laik a bullet oot o' a gun. By jeengs ah'll bet youse any money she wid have been tasty," he said.

A strike settlement looked imminent as the *Dawn Hunter* and *Bounteous* loaded their final cargoes at Campbeltown the following week. Both vessels had completed refitting work between the Econobuys runs and were ready to return to fishing in any case. Gleaming like new, the boats painted a delightful picture as they steamed out of Campbeltown Harbour bound for Red Bay, each carrying a substantial consignment of eggs.

Unloading operations were well underway on the Irish side when a minibus packed with stern-faced men arrived alongside the Econobuys lorry. Without a word being spoken, a dozen or so wildcat seamen strikers ripped open the big cardboard egg cases and proceeded to pelt both boats and crews at random. Apparently a local had informed the Larne branch of the Seamen's Union of the goings on and the strikers were out for vengeance. Wullie and Jamie were left with no alternative but to let go the mooring ropes and make hastily for the open sea, to the echoing chorus of "scabs, scabs, yer nothin' but scabs."

The *Dawn Hunter* and *Bounteous* presented a sorry sight on their return to Campbeltown. Wullie was almost in tears as he surveyed his beloved boat, which would have to be treated from stem to stern with a high-pressure steam washer and repainted. To make matters worse, an official looking gentleman dressed in a pinstriped suit requested an urgent meeting with Wullie. He introduced himself as Captain David Pemberton, of the Department of Transport, and wished to know if it was the case that the *Dawn Hunter* had been shipping cargo to Northern Ireland for payment on a regular basis for the past few weeks.

"Aye, an' hoot aboot it," replied Wullie with a hint of uncharacteristic truculence.

"Oh, it's just that you will be required to have your vessel surveyed officially for a load line certificate, Skipper Maclean. See to it at once."

Wullie worked out in a flash that such arrangements would cost him in the region of £2000. He looked down at his pride and joy lying forlornly at her moorings and turned to his engineer.

"Cameron, fae noo on the only cargo that'll be on that boat is fush. Supposin' ah wis offered a king's ransom there'll nivver be another egg, or tins o' bully beef or wumman's knickers doon that howld ivver again.

PART TWO

DONAL' STOTT'S BROO...
AND OTHER GLORIOUSLY NAMED PLACES

As was mentioned in one of my previous books, *Life with the Coal Tar*, Campbeltown fishermen of old were very active in providing names for even the smallest *port* or indentation on the rugged Kintyre coastline.

Lots of these names roll off the tongue in a quite magical manner and I am pleased to be able to list some 25 places in the immediate vicinity of Campbeltown.

I am indebted to Mr Billy Gilchrist, of Campbeltown, for providing the required information. Few can be better qualified than Billy since he has an intimate knowledge of the coastline surrounding Campbeltown - the result of years of lobster and line fishing close inshore. Indeed, I have joyous memories of being allowed, with his nephew William Gilchrist, formerly of the town, to accompany him on mackerel fishing expeditions during long summer evenings aboard his trim little boat, the *Will Reward*. The excitement of hand hauling six *darra* hooks with a wildly thrashing mackerel on each one was to me, as a 12-year-old, quite overwhelming.

The following locations can be identified by referring to the appropriate number on the chart, which has been reproduced by permission of the Royal Navy's Hydrographic Office .

1 Crochnaheilan; 2 Richmond Slip; 3 Dougie's Bay; 4 Joiner's Shed; 5 The Gauger's Rock (named after a whisky gauger); 6 The Paling; 7 The Plank; 8 Porter's Glen; 9 Andie's Burn; 10 Rocky Burn; 11 Peggy's Rock; 12 The Muckle Rocks; 13 Bella's Bay; 14 Neck o' the Dhorlinn; 15 Donal' Stott's Broo (brow); 16 The Anvil; 17 THe Riddlings; 18 The Coulyam; 19 Portnacaple; 20 McVoories; 21 The Sheep Hoose; 22 The Yella (yellow) Point 23 The Long Point; 24 The Boat Hoose; 25 The Flet Rock.

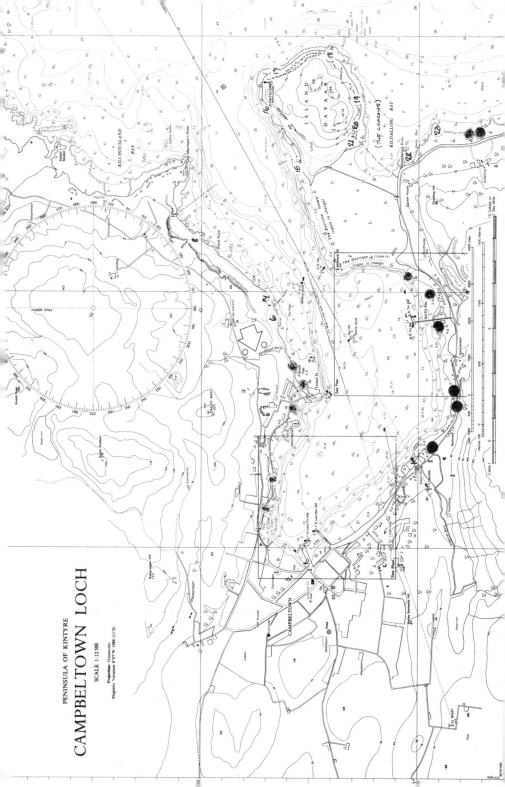

CAMPBELTOWN LOCH

PENINSULA OF KINTYRE

SCALE 1:12,500

Projection: Gnomonic.

Magnetic Variation 8°07′W 1988 (11′E)

THE CAMPBELTOWN FISHERMEN'S ALPHABET

(Sung to the tune of *Master MacGrath*)

A for the anchor we chap on the bow
B for the boy who kicks up a row
C for the cable, a good friend and true, and
D for the deck that shelters our crew

Chorus
So merry, so merry, so merry are we
No mortals on earth like a fisher at sea
Hard east there, hard west there, you're right through my net
You're the stupidest fellow that I've ever met

E for the engine that runs very well
F for the forecastle where we do dwell
G for the grub that we all do eat, and
H for the herring that cannot be beat

I for ideas they're not very plain
J for the jumpers to keep out the rain
K for the kettle we use every day, and
L for the loaves we all stow away

M for the meshing we all love to see
N for the net we cast in the sea
O for the oil we burn or we waste, and
P for the pump that we oft grab in haste

Q for the quarter that our gear runs o'er
R for the reef-points not used as in yore
S for the sail not used much of late, and
T for the tiller to steer our boat straight

U for the urchins we take for a treat
V for the vessels that we often meet
W for the winch for which we all pine
But the last three letters I can't put to rhyme

The above was penned in the mid 1930's by the late Peter Gilchrist, of Campbeltown, who operated the fishing vessel *Janet* with his brother William. He was also responsible for the lyrics of the song *In Campbeltown Once More* (below). This song was dedicated to his sister, Agnes, (later Mrs Stewart McKiernan) though he refers to her as *Nancy*. The rousing tune to which the song is sung is similar to that used by Irish folk bands when singing *The Holy Ground*
Mrs Jennifer Kelly, of Campbeltown, is a grandniece of the composer and still has in her possession the originals, albeit slightly dog-eared. I am grateful to Jennifer for providing the information and verse.

IN CAMPBELTOWN ONCE MORE

Fare-ye-well my Nancy, a thousand times adieu
Fare-ye-well my Nancy, but I must part from you
I must part from you dear one, you're the lassie I adore
But we will live in hope to meet in Cam'eltown
once more

Chorus:
In Cam'eltown once more my boys, in Cam'eltown once more
Yes we will live in hope to meet in Cam'eltown once more

Now the storm is raging, we can see it coming on
The clouds are bent to westward, we can scarcely see the moon
Our goodly ship is tossed about and our riggings sadly torn
But we will live in hope to meet in Cam'eltown once more

Repeat first chorus

Yes, now the storm is raging, the waves are lashing high
But bravely stems our gallant barque, the salt tear dims my eye
The salt tear dims my eye my boys, but we will reach the shore
And we will live in hope to meet in Cam'eltown once more

Repeat first chorus

Now the storm is ended and we are safe at last
We've got the Trench Point now in view, Davaar Light we have passed
And soon we'll get our anchor down when we get to the shore
And we are back again my boys, in Cam'eltown once more

Chorus:
In Cam'eltoon once more my boys, in Cam'eltown once more
And we are back again my boys, in Cam'eltown once more

Yes now the storm is over, and we are safe on shore
We'll drink success to our sweethearts, wives and the lassies we adore
We'll call for glasses merrily and make the tavern roar
And when our money is all spent, we'll plough the seas for more

Chorus:
We'll plough the seas for more my boys, we'll plough the seas for more
And when our money is all spent, we'll plough the seas for more.

BETTY MCNIVEN AND 'THE FLIGHT'

It gives me pleasure to reproduce part of an article written by the editor of *Kintyre Magazine*, Angus Martin, who is the author of the quite outstanding book, *The Ring Net Fishermen*. In the piece, Angus refers to a unique poem with a fishing theme written by a Campbeltown schoolgirl in the late 1930's:

In a letter to The Campbeltown Courier, I asked, among other things, for information on the author of a poem, which incorporated the names of 19 Campbeltown fishing boats to tell the story of an elopement. I knew only that the author's name was McNiven and thought she had been a schoolgirl when she wrote the poem.

The response was excellent. A copy of the poem, with the author's full name, Betty McNiven, was received from Mr Jim McGeachy on the following day, and on the day after that I met Mr Harry Lavery, who was able to tell me a good deal about Betty McNiven herself, "amazed" at seeing the first lines of her poem quoted in the Courier.

That poem, The Flight, is well crafted and memorable.

The Scottish artist and poet, Ian Hamilton Findlay, has produced found poems using only fishing boat names, and here, in Green Waters, is the best known of them

Green Waters
Blue Spray
Grayfish

Anna T
Karen B
Netta Croan

Constant Star
Daystar
Satinwood

Starlit Waters
Moonlt Waters
Drift.

It is certainly a lovely and unusual piece, but Betty McNiven was there before him! Bad poems are almost never remembered. Betty McNiven's poem was good enough to catch the imagination of a public – albeit local and fishing-related – and I am delighted to publish it again, and also to recognise the author, because The Flight has been heading down the road towards a final resting place in the amorphousness of folklore.

After she finished in the Grammar School, Betty went on to the University of Glasgow, graduated M.A. in English and History, and then did a year's teacher training at Dundee Training College.

Able only to obtain supply teaching work in Campbeltown – at the Wee Grammar and Millknowe Primary Schools – she eventually got a permanent teaching post at Kinlochleven. It was there that she met her late husband, Ian Campbell Cassidy, a native of the village. They were married in Campbeltown in 1943 by the Rev B.B. Blackwood and lived thereafter in Inverlochy and Fort William. Betty later taught for about 10 years in Caol Primary School, near Fort William.

As to the poem itself, Mrs Cassidy writes: 'I was then Betty McNiven, a member of Angus MacVicar's journalism class at the night school in the thirties, just before the Second World War.

'I owed my interest in the fishing fleet and other boats to my uncle, the late James Lavery, who had himself once owned a sailing vessel, the William and Leigh, which traded among the Western Isles and to Northern Ireland before the puffers arrived.

'When Angus MacVicar decided that we must publish a magazine, I decided to write something about the fishing fleet, but did not think there would be much interest in it. There were many more boats in the fleet but a lot of the names didn't fit in.'

THE FLIGHT

The King Bird fled with the Fairy Queen
Into the Golden Dawn
The Maris Stella watched their flight
While the rest of the world slept on.

The Busy Bee was the first to wake
And she went to the Mystical Rose
'They have gone,' she cried, 'What can we do?
Perhaps Bengullion knows.'

'Let the Frigate Bird pursue,' he cried, 'in her garb of Silver Grey.
And swift as a Crimson Arrow sped
The beautiful ship away.

Then Blue Bird said: I am as swift as light;
Nulli Secundus am I.
I will bring them back or return no more',
And the Falcon made reply.

Nil Desperandum; I will go forth
on this Enterprise with you.'
But the Goddess Felicia shook her head
And helped the lovers through.

And they came no more to their old Sweet Home,
Where the Kingfisher roves at will,
But the Ave Maria's sweet notes recall
The loch they both love stiill.

THE DO'S AND DON'Ts

Fishermen throughout the U.K. and Eire have always been a superstitious breed of men. Indeed, Scots fishermen in particular seem even more inclined towards the beliefs, little rituals and the prohibited usage of certain words. The Campbeltown branch of the industry is no different and, although idolatrous practices obviously never took place, generations of local fishermen have believed in the various taboos with a potent sincerity.

As a fisherman's son, I was introduced early to the everyday words which, from the dark and distant past, did not figure in the family vocabulary. *Pig, rabbit, salmon, rat,* four ordinary little words that are uttered many thousands of times in the course of a day. However, these same words will never be heard on a Campbeltown fishing boat or in a fishing household. The respective alternatives are *doorkie, bunny, redfish (or buhlly)* and *long-tailed fella'.*

I actually found myself in trouble as a school pupil when I refused to orally deliver *rabbit* during a class enunciation exercise. The lack of understanding of fishing beliefs by a harassed teacher cost me a memorable sore hand when I was belted with the dreaded tawse, and my classmates were both puzzled and impressed by this brave act of martyrdom.

Some fishermen have actually been known to return home without even reaching the harbour — the result of an encounter with a redheaded woman or a *man of the cloth.* Paradoxically, though, many fishermen are married to redheads and attend church on a regular basis.

When leaving harbour, the boat must not turn against the sun and should make a starboard sweep to follow its path, a manoeuvre that obviously causes problems occasionally in congested berthing areas.

Swan Vestas matches, or, indeed, any product that features the graceful bird must never be carried on the vessel. Similarly, a white-handled knife is another item with a total onboard ban. Knives of any kind should not be stuck into the mast, as this is considered to be the heart of the boat. Knives and forks cannot be crossed on a plate at the completion of a meal, during which all headgear must be removed.

The borrowing of salt is not allowed and the burning of bread, no matter how stale, is another deadly sin.

Old shoes or boots retrieved from the deep are always kept as a talisman. If a jumper is inadvertently put on back to front, then this is regarded as a good omen, although a wet bonnet singed while drying at the cabin fire is immediately discarded and a new hat sought.

The minor personal operation of toe or fingernail clipping cannot be undertaken on the Sabbath and it is regarded as bad luck to comb one's hair immediately prior to going to bed. I would imagine, though, that the last thing on an exhausted fisherman's mind after a lengthy stint on deck would be his concern for tonsorial elegance. When shoes or boots are being polished, the footwear should never be allowed to rest on a table.

Seagulls, especially the herring variety, must never be harmed as they are said to represent long-departed fishermen in the afterlife.

Many fishermen also take great care when naming a boat to ensure that the letters do not add up to 13.

Green, for some reason, is a colour regarded with total aversion by many fishers when it comes to boat painting time. However, various vessels owned over the years by my uncle, skipper Ronnie Brownie of Carradale, sailed in an unchanging livery of resplendent dark green. The colour certainly bode him no ill, as this scallop fisherman was one of the fishing village's most consistently successful earners over a period of three decades.

PHOTOGRAPHIC SECTION

Most of the following 100 photographs deal mainly with the progression of herring fishing in the Clyde and Scottish West Coast during the 20th century. This photographic record contains rare pictures taken throughout the decades and catalogues the development of the wooden-built ring netters, which were eventually superseded by herring pair trawlers and purse seiners.

The last traditional herring ringer built in Scotland, the 60-foot *Alliance (CN 187)*, was launched for my family from the Girvan boatyard of Alexander Noble and Sons on March 11, 1974. She spent one brief period only - in the autumn of that year - at the ring net in partnership with the Carradale boat *Silver Cloud (CN 267)*, before going on to pursue a successful career at prawn/fish trawling, scallop dredging and herring pair trawling.

Bigger, bulkier boats gradually took over the role of herring catchers and the graceful lines of the ring netters became an increasingly rarer sight.

The largest purpose built Clyde herring boat was the 86-foot purse seiner *Pathfinder (BA 188)* constructed in steel for the late Skipper Bert Andrew, of Maidens.

Sadly, herring fishing in the Clyde from the ports of Campbeltown, Carradale, Tarbert, Dunure and Girvan has become a thing of the past and a greatly reduced fleet concentrates on prawn trawling, scallop dredging and creeling.

THE CAMPBELTOWN RING NET FLEET

Much of the very considerable prosperity generated in Campbeltown during the 19th and early 20th centuries was due to whisky distilling and, in no small measure, herring fishing.

The population of the burgh at the turn of the century was 8300, nearly 3000 more than it is today. Statistics from the year 1888 show that there was an astonishing total of 646 herring skiffs employing 2185 fishermen registered at Campbeltown, although there was a substantial reduction in the number of these smaller boats as the new century progressed. However, thanks to the technological advances in the ring net method - largely pioneered in the 1920's and 1930's by the legendary Robert Robertson - the Campbeltown fleet was the envy of many. As a direct consequence of his endeavours, the town was, by

1950, home to arguably the finest fleet of ring netters in the country. They were built in East and West Coast yards with famous names - Weatherhead, Noble, Forbes, Reekie, Millar and McMillan. Indeed, some of them were well ahead of their time. Listed below are the names of herring boats taken from a 1950's CN register, which includes several from neighbouring Carradale.

Florian (CN 2)
Watercress (CN 3)
Elma (CN 25)
Westering Home (CN 26)
Moira (CN 33)
Nobles Again (CN 37)
Irma (CN 45)
Almanzora (CN 54)
Acacia (CN 56)
Seafarer (CN 77)
Janet Lang (CN 84)
Kestrel (CN 93)
Kittiwake (CN94)
Falcon (CN 97)
Nan McMurrar (CN 105)
Escallonia (CN 110)
Marion 2 (CN 111)
Margaret Rose (CN 115)
Marie Elspeth (CN 116)
Regina Maris (CN 118)
Golden Dawn (CN 119)
Lily Oak (CN 131)
Endeavour (CN 132)
Boy Danny (CN 142)
Amalthea ((CN 143)
Stella Maris (CN 158)
Anne Philomena (CN 159)
Rhu-na-Gal (CN 163)
Kathleen (CN 164)
Fiona (CN 165)
Harvest Queen (CN 167)

Golden Fleece (CN 170)
Maid of Morven (CN 177)
Annie (CN 178)
Morag Bhan (CN 183)
Margaret Newton (CN 184)
Maureen (CN 185)
Elizabeth Campbell (CN 186)
Mary McLean (CN 193)
Jessie (CN 194)
Jessie MacKinnon (CN 196)
Florentine (CN 197)
Golden Hind (CN 199)
Bengullion (CN 229)
Nobles (CN 236)
Felicia (CN 237)
May (CN 243)
Amy Harris (CN 249)
Glen Carradale (CN 253)
Mairi Bhan (CN 259)
Kingbird (CN 264)
Queen of the Fleet (CN 269)

The Campbeltown herring skiff *Mary McLellan* *(121 CN)* leaving Campbeltown Loch for the fishing grounds

The Tarbert herring fleet making for the famous Loch Fyne in this 1894 photograph

An unidentified Tarbert skiff pictured at the village harbour in 1895

An 1896 photograph of Campbeltown fisherman Neil Brodie, seen here aboard his vessel *Helen.* The Brodie family owned a total of seven herring skiffs.

Carradale herring skiffs at the Waterfoot estuary of the River Carra in September 1910.

The herring skiff CN 668 (name unknown) being poled into Waterfoot circa 1910.

Another unusual shot of the Carradale boats at Waterfoot. Note the ring net 'drying poles' in the background.

This photograph was taken at Torrisdale, near Carradale, where a number of boats were based.

Preparing for another herring hunt at Portrigh Bay, Carradale

Campbeltown herring fisherman, who also served as lifeboat crewmen, during a fundraising drive in 1912. (l to r) William Gilchrist, Charles Durnin, Malcolm Newlands and a youthful Duncan Newlands, who was destined to become a celebrated coxswain of Campbeltown Lifeboat.

Campbeltown's pioneering ring net fisherman, Robert *Hoodie* Robertson, had the **Falcon** built at St. Monaance in 1921. She was the UK's first ever canoe sterned ringer.

Hall Street and the Old Quay, Campbeltown, during the 1920's, where women cured and packed thousands of barrels of locally caught herring for export.

Robert Robertson had the *Nil Desperandum* designed with a forward wheelhouse. She came from the same St. Monance boatyard of Walter Reekie & Sons in 1928 but the innovative design met with mixed success

The Tarbert skiff *Flying Fish* is pictured here discharging herring at her home port

An Ardrishaig ring net crew - probably the last in the village - prepares to take the net aboard.

A study of an unidentified Tarbert ringer taken from Harbour Street.

Overhauling the net on a Carradale boat during the 1930's. The gentleman wearing the soft hat is John *Dodge* Galbraith.

The Carradale ringer **Alban** is seen here following her annual refit.

The larger and more sophisticated design of the ring netter in the late 1930's is exemplified in this photograph taken at Waterfoot, Carradale. In the forefront is the *Cluaran.*

The Carradale boat *Irma,* skippered by *Jamie* Campbell, was particularly successful in this ring off the Brown Head, Isle of Arran, in 1937.

The McDougall family's *Mairead,* lying at her mooring directly opposite Tarbert Fish Quay.

Carradale ring net vessels photographed at Jamaica Bridge, in the heart of Glasgow, early in 1939. They had sailed up the River Clyde to protest at poor herring prices and to highlight their campaign for the construction of a new pier.

Crew members of the Tarbert ringer **Village Belle** pose for the photographer. The boat was one of a pair owned by the successful Jackson brothers.

The former Campbeltown vessel **Kingfisher** pictured in her new home port of Tarbert, following her purchase by the McFarlane family.

A view of the original Carradale Pier. Note some of the boats are still rigged for drift net fishing.

Campbeltown Harbour jam packed with ring netters which were taking part in the 1949 Brown Head, Arran, fishing. There are a few East Coast vessels to be seen, but the very great majority of the boats were local.

An astonishing sight at Tarbert, Loch Fyne, circa 1950. A huge fleet of herring ringers anchors for the day before pursuing the Loch Fyne fishery during the hours of darkness.

On the beach at Campbeltown. The boats were moored bows in and became high and dry as the tide receded in order that antifouling operations could be carried out.

Launch of the **Golden Gleam** from the Dickie of Tarbert boatyard. She was, unfortunately, later wrecked on a reef on the west side of Mull.

The Tarbert ringer *Pride of the Clyde* slides into the water for the first time at her launch from the St. Monance yard of Walter Reekie.

Varnished ringers photographed in the inner basin of Campbeltown's Old Quay   The boat
with the bow fender is the *Maid of Morvern.*

Dressed up for the Gala Day as part of Campbeltown's Civic Week in 1952 are the
Golden Hind (under way) and the *Mary McLean* (foreground)

The Campbeltown ring netter *Regina Maris* slices through a rare flat calm sea on her way to the Clyde herring grounds.

Overhauling the net on a Carradale boat during the 1930's. The gentleman wearing the soft hat is John *Dodge* Galbraith.

Campbeltown and Carradale ring netters used Mallaig as a landing port during the winter *North* fishing on the Outer Hebrides grounds. The Carradale boat **Elizabeth Campbell** is pictured centre, while the Campbeltown pair **Boy Danny** and **Margaret Rose** can be seen in the background.

The former Campbeltown ringer **Margaret Newton** was renamed **Village Belle 111** following her sale to the Jackson brothers of Tarbert.

Photographed at her home port of Tarbert is the 53-footer *Margarita,* a Weatherhead vessel owned by the McAlpine family.

Carradale harbour following its extensive refurbishment. In the foreground is the lobster boat *Marlene.* The ring netters are (from left to right) are *Watercress, Florentine* and *Maid of the Mi* In the background are *Amy Harris* and *Escallonia.*

Hauling a ring on the Carradale boat *Florentine* during a bonanza fishing at Carradale Bay in 1960. (Left to right): Donald McAllister, Bill McMillan, Ronnie Brownie, Donald McConnachie and John Ramsay. Four local boats, *Irma, Florentine, Amy Harris* and *Escallonia* worked as a team during this period.

Three members of the McConnachie family photographed at the conclusion of a successful ring on the *Florentine*. (Left to right): Donald, Walter and John

A big ring of herring taken during the Uist daylight fishing of 1961 being brailed aboard the *Storm Drift*, the neighbour vessel being *Summer Rose.*

Oops, wrong species! The *New Dawn,* of Dunure, pictured in Ayr landing a huge shot of saithe, which are also know variously as *peuchties, podlies* or *jacks.*

study of the **Nobles Again** (left) and **Fiona** shortly afer their annual refits at Campbeltown in 1962. (Note there is no Woolworth store at the head of the Old Quay).

One year later and Woolworth is in business in the town. In the foreground (left to right) are the *loira* and **Golden Hind.** In the background (bow-in) is the **Mary Mclean** and the **Star of Hope** can be seen lying against the sea wall.

A few of the Carradale boats at *The Burn,* the local name for the sheltered Waterfoot anchorage at the mouth of the River Carra. Left to right: ***Silver Quest, Escallonia*** and ***Watercress.***

Another favourite Carradale beaching site for refit work was *The Quay Beach,* conveniently sited close by the pier. Scraping work has started on the ***Florentine*** (left). The other boat is the McMillan family's ***Maid of the Mist***

The sweet lines of the ring netter are exemplified in this picture of the Carradale vessel *Bairns Pride,* seen here discharging herring at Tarbert.

At rest for the day at Tarbert are (left to right): *Margarita, Ann Marie, Mary McLean, Boy Danny* and *Caledonia.*

The Tarbert boat *Village Maid 2,* owned by the Jackson family, entering Mallaig Harbour with a good shot of herring on board. Note there is a quantity of boxed herring on deck.

Some of the Campbeltown ring netters, all in immaculate order, seen here at the inner harbour in late June 1962.

Another shot of the inner harbour, Campbeltown, showing(foreground): *Stella Maris, Boy Danny (CN 142)* and *Mary McLean.*

Hosing down the Carradale vessel *Shemaron* on the completion of herring landing operations at Tarbert.

Pictured leaving Girvan in the teeth of a north-westerly gale is the Tarbert boat *Village Belle 3.*

A fine study of the **Village Maid 2,** also photographed steaming out of Girvan.

A master at work. The ring net snakes over the quarter of the Maidens ringer *Wistaria,* during Uist daylight fishing. One of the Clyde's most successful ring net fishermen of modern times, the legendary Billy Sloan, skippered her.

The man himself: Billy Sloan at the winch of the *Wistaria* during discharging work at Tarbert.

The Ayrshire ring netters *Watchful* and *Saffron (BA 182)* brailing herring aboard both boats from a bulging net in Loch Carnan, North Uist. This 1967 daylight fishing was something of a bonanza for the boats.

Running trials off Carradale in 1967 is the *Ocean Maid,* built at Fairlie for the McMillan family to replace the *Fair Maid.* Powered by a Caterpillar 240hp engine, she was the last new ring netter to be built for the village.

One of Scotland's biggest ever ringers, the 65-foot Dunure-owned *New Dawn, i*s seen here in Loch Ness on her maiden trip home to the Clyde from the Herd and McKenzie yard at Buckie. The vessel was built for the Munro family.

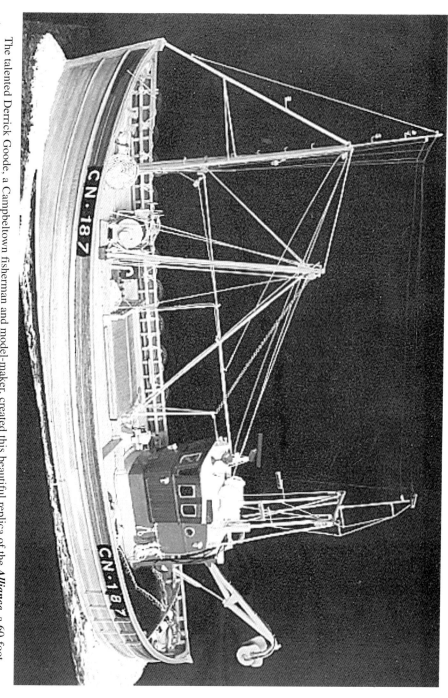

The talented Derrick Goode, a Campbeltown fisherman and model-maker, created this beautiful replica of the *Alliance*, a 60-foot ringer/trawler built for my family by Alexander Noble & Sons, Girvan. Launched in March 1974, the *Alliance* was was the last ever ring net vessel built and her completion brought to an end the golden era of such graceful and eye-pleasing purpose built herring boats

PAIR-TRAWLING FOR HERRING

By the late 1960's, ring net operations in the Firth of Clyde and further afield in Scottish West Coast waters had become the exception rather than the rule. The pair trawling method, developed by Norwegian fishermen, was being adopted by their North East Scots counterparts in increasing numbers. The pair trawl had a critical advantage over the ring net in that herring could be taken from far greater depths, often with spectacular results, since the gear could be easily adjusted to fish according to where the species swam.

Modern sophisticated vessels, much larger and more powerful than the traditional ring netter, pursued the pair trawling method from ports such as Peterhead, Fraserburgh and Gardenstown.

When the East Coast men arrived in the Firth of Clyde, their presence met with considerable opposition, amid claims that the pair-trawl would cause untold damage to herring stocks and other species by the slaughter of immature fish. The Carradale branch of the Clyde Fishermens' Association – the village from where ring netting was last practised in the 1970's – was particularly active in trying to ban pair trawling. *The Crofters,* as they are collectively known, were unsuccessful and the only legislation introduced – probably too late - was a quota system that restricted each pair to a set allowable catch.

Skippers of the larger ring net boats that were equipped with more powerful engines realised with reluctance that in order to compete, they would have to take the expensive step of fitting out for pair trawling and, it has to be said, a fair number of Clyde men became proficient at the job.

However, the lamentable fact is that there are now no herring boats of any kind making a living in the area and, with the cessation of ring netting, a way of life was wiped out, not only in the Clyde, but also among the Hebridean islands. Of the fishermen left *at the job*, only a small number have been involved in ring netting and it would be a difficult task to crew a few pairs of boats in the Clyde with experienced men. It has been asserted that if pair trawling had been banned and ring netting allowed to continue, a viable herring fishery could well have been sustained until the present day.

Among the first in the Clyde ring net fleet to attempt herring pair trawling were the Gardner-powered *Ocean Gem* (white) and *Pathfinder,* skippered by the brothers Wattie and Bert Andrew, of Maidens, Ayrshire.

The Girvan boat *Saffron,* skippered by the forward thinking Angus McCrindle Snr., was another Clyde air-trawl pioneer. The crew is seen here, circa 1971, hauling a shot of 40 crans at Lochboisdale, South Uist.

The bigger, more powerful *Saffron* replaced her 1951-built older sister in 1973. Angus McCrindle Jnr. skippered this boat with great success at both herring fishing and prawn/fish trawling.

The *Alliance* fitted out as a herring pair trawler steaming down Campbeltown Loch to begin another week's work with her neighbour boat *Aquila.*

The *New Dawn* rigged as a herring pair trawler.

Grieve Gemmell's *Storm Drift 2* was another Noble-built ringer to convert successfully to pair trawling.

Looking resplendent after a thorough paint job is the *Storm Drift's* neighbour, the *Britannia*, skippered by the late Billy Gibson.

The *Marie* was another Gardner-powered ringer that was re-engined with a 365hp Caterpillar, which enabled her to participate in herring pair trawling.

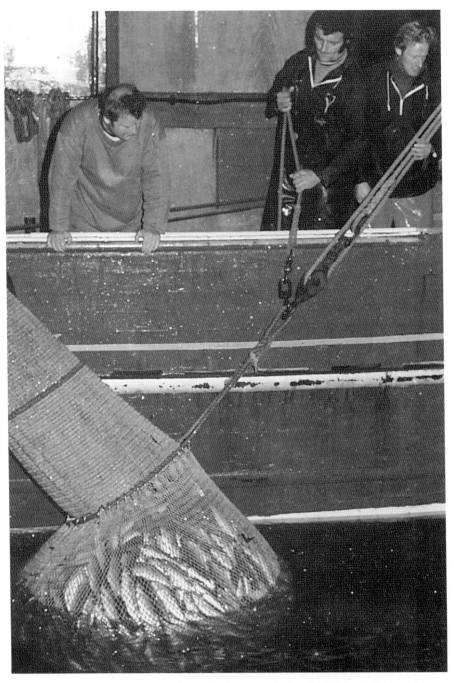

The business end of the herring pair-trawl being connected to the lifting tackle aboard the Carradale vessel *Silver Fern* following a haul in Kilbrannan Sound.

Safely aboard: a full lift of bonnie big Clyde herring which, when this picture was taken in the 1970's, were fetching anything up to an incredible £80 per unit (100 kilograms)

Another fine example of a Noble of Girvan pair-trawler is the 55-foot *Spindrift,* built for the McLean brothers, of Maidens, in 1974.

This is what it is all about! The heavily laden pair team of *Aquila* (foreground) and *Alliance* alongside at Tarbert in the mid 1980's with a combined catch of 650 units (65 tonnes) of good quality sprats.

The Ayr-registered herring trawler *Lunaria*, which was skippered by the well-known *Lintie* Anderson, is pictured at her weekend berth in Troon.

The Dutch-built **Hercules,** skippered by Hugh Edgar, looking spick and span after her annual re fit as she heads out of port.

The steel purse-seiner **Pathfinder** was built in the 1980's for Skipper Bert Andrew to replace the wooden ringer/trawler of the same name. Sadly, Bert died later in tragic circumstances.

One of Ayrshire's most respected fishermen, Bob McCutcheon, skippered the 73-foot *Chrysolite*.

The *Chrysolite's* partner was the equally gutsy *Silver Quest 2*

PRAWN TRAWLING IN THE CLYDE

In the 1950's, when herring ring netters made occasional forays to the seine-net method in pursuit of demersal fish, a real bugbear to fishermen were the huge heaps of prawns that sometimes came aboard with the cod, haddock or whiting. The fish had to be carefully separated from the pink crustaceans before the latter were shovelled back over the side by the thousand, treated as an unwanted nuisance.

However, in the fickle epicurean world, this species known variously as Norway lobsters, Dublin Bay Prawns or Nephrops, suddenly became fashionable in top eating-houses and fishermen treated the hitherto loathsome by-catch in a different light. More and more Scots fishermen from many West and East Coast ports joined in and, in the Firth of Clyde, a fleet of prawn trawlers, including many 40-footers, grew rapidly. The steadier earnings from prawn fishing compared to the uncertainty of hunting the increasingly elusive herring shoals eventually saw the ring net fleet spending half of each year at the trawling. And by the late 1960's, every Campbeltown ring net boat in the 88hp to 132hp range had converted to prawn trawling on a permanent basis. As the years passed, the ringers were either decommissioned or sold off for private use and the great majority of vessels in Campbeltown, Carradale and Tarbert are now modern dedicated prawn trawlers. They are fitted with shelter decks, hydraulic cranes and winches and equipped with a mind-boggling array of electronic fish finding and navigational aids.

Prawn trawling is carried on extensively in the Irish Sea, Firth of Clyde, Scottish West Coast including the Minches and in the North Sea.

Some of the original 40-foot Campbeltown prawn trawlers - vessels that played a huge part in the development of the lucrative prawn industry. Foreground, left to right: *Star of Hope 2* and *Kia-Ora.* Incidentally, the *Star of Hope 2* was the first boat to be built by Noble of Girvan as the *Margaret Stephen.* The three boats in the second tier are the **Brighter Morn, Westward** and *Sea Nymph.* Visible in the background are the *Girl Ann* and *Evening Star.*

One of the early vessels owned by the renowned Cecil Finn was the **Brighter Morn (ex Nimrod),** seen here stripped down for her annual refit alongside the ringer **Regina Maris.** In the background is the former Campbeltown vessel **Annie,** under new ownership as **Fair Morn (BA 54)**

Painting time at Tarbert on the beach near the former Dickie's boatyard for the local vessel ***Oor Lassie,*** skippered by James McNab.

Coming alongside at Tarbert is the Dickie-built ***Nancy Glen,*** skippered then by Duncan McDougall. His son, John *Tar* McDougall now commands the ***Nancy Glen 3*** and is among the village's top skippers.

Secured safely for the weekend in the Crinan Canal basin are the prawners *Silver Fern,* of Tarbert, and the Inverness-registered Avoch-owned *Primrose.*

One of the Ayrshire ringers that could not meet the considerable horsepower requirements of the herring pair trawl, the *Valhalla,* latterly concentrated on prawn trawling.

Another classic example of a ringer turned prawner was the Dunure boat *Fair Wind,* although she enjoyed a successful early herring career. She is seen here in Troon following the installation of a new wheelhouse.

ne of the few decommissioned ringer/prawners to be saved from the chainsaw was the *Stella Maris 4* of Campbeltown, which was built by Weatherhead as the *Watchful* for the Sloan family of Maidens. e has been restored to her original condition and can be seen at an Ayrshire maritime heritage centre.

A far cry from her former role as a Carradale ring netter, the *Florentine* pictured in her new guise as a prawn/white fish trawler following her sale to Fleetwood owners.

A peaceful weekend scene in the 1980's at West Loch Tarbert. The former ferry pier is used as a seasonal base by Clyde prawn vessels.

The prawner *Jeannie Stella,* an immaculately maintained 40-foot boat that was built mainly by her owner, Peter McKichen, of Portincaple, Loch Long.

The former Carradale vessel *Adoration* takes aboard a heavy codend (possibly holding a boulder!) following a haul in the Whitestone Bank area of Kilbrannan Sound.

Skipper John Galbraith's state of the art GRP prawn trawler *Sapphire* seen here approaching her home port of Carradale.

Skipper Galbraith supervises the lifting aboard of a big haul of prawns on one of his previous vessels, the *Silver Bell.*

The development of prawn fishing has seen a dramatic change in the size and design of boats deployed. This photograph shows the 66-foot *Nova Spero,* of Campbeltown, which was bought by my brothers Robert and Willie to replace the *Alliance,* following her sale to Irish owners.

Another example of a modern prawn trawler is the *Primrose,* formerly owned by Ian Smith, of Tarbert.

SCALLOP DREDGING

Scallop dredging is another fishing method that was developed on a large scale following the demise of the once mighty herring industry.

Scallops, better known locally as clams, have become increasingly popular, albeit a shade expensive, in restaurants all over Britain and have found favour recently with television celebrity chefs.

They are much thinner on the ground than in the early days of heavy fishing, and the scallop fleet now consists mainly of boats that do not pursue any other method. Many other vessels at one time fished for scallops on a seasonal basis when other species were scarce.

The main disadvantage of scallop dredging is the wear and tear on boat and gear. Heavy metal dredges with sharp toothbars are used to dig the scallops out of their sandy and stony habitat, often resulting in piles of mini rocks and shingle being brought on board along with the shells. Indeed, it is easy to spot a scalloper by the hard-worked look presented by the boat, and this is probably another reason why skippers prefer other fishing methods.

When the death knell sounded on the ring net fishing, all the Campbeltown boats turned to prawn and queen scallop trawling but the nearby Carradale fleet showed a strange reluctance to do likewise. Most of the boats in the village were fitted out for dredging and followed this type of fishing for years, although the scallop's scarcity has seen a gradual swing to bottom trawling.

There are, however, still several full-time scallop dredgers in the fleet.

My first berth! Ronnie Brownie's scalloper *Brighter Hope,* which holds many happy memories for me. What she lacked in refinements, she made up for in character.

The *Bonnie Lass 2,* another of Uncle Ronnie's boats that enjoyed a successful scallop career.

The **Bonnie Lass 3,** which was owned by Ronnie up until his retirement. The Gerrard of Arbroath-built vessel was a familiar sight in Clyde and Sound of Jura waters for a long time.

Looking remarkably tidy for a scalloper is Jimmy *Dimbo* Milne's *Sea Otter,* pictured here at Troon.

The former Carradale scallop dredger *Silver Fern* has changed hands several times since her launch in 1971. She is presently fishing from Tarbert, Loch Fyne.

A peaceful scene at Gigha Pier as the Manx scallopers **Valonia** *and* **Peter M** *tie up for the night.*

Freddy Gillies at work on MV LOCHRANZA 1999